ALLAN MORRISON is a proli
include *Goanae No Dae Th*
Haud ma Chips Ah've Drap
Haud that Bus and *Shoul*
His media appearances include *The One Show*, *The Riverside Show*, *Out of Doors* and *Good Morning Scotland*. He is involved in charity work and after-dinner speaking, and is a member of his local Rotary club. Allan enjoys hill-walking, sport and travel, and is a keen football supporter. He and his wife live in the west of Scotland, and he is the proud grandfather of four grandchildren.

Kerryoans up the Clyde!

it could only happen on the *Waverley*

ALLAN MORRISON
with illustrations by
BOB DEWAR

Luath Press Limited
EDINBURGH
www.luath.co.uk

First published 2021

ISBN: 978-1-910022-71-9

The author's right to be identified as author of this book
under the Copyright, Designs and Patents Act 1988 has been asserted.

Printed and bound by
Clays Ltd., Bungay

Typeset in 12 point Sabon by
Main Point Books, Edinburgh

© Allan Morrison 2021

ON BEHALF OF

CAPTAIN LIZZIE

AND THE CREW,

LET ME WELCOME YOU

ABOARD

THE PADDLE STEAMER

WAVERLEY!

Contents

Acknowledgements 9

1 Meet Big Lizzie, Master of the *Waverley* 11

2 Introducing the *Waverley* 15

3 Master and Commander 21

Waverley Chuckles 33

4 The Wedding 39

Waverley Chuckles 57

5 Off to Tighnabruaich 63

Waverley Chuckles 75

6 A Whale of a Time 81

Waverley Chuckles 95

7 Passengers Young and Old 99

Waverley Chuckles 113

8 The Offer! 117

Waverley Chuckles 135

9 The History of the *Waverley* 139

Summary of *Waverley* Statistical Data 145

Eventful Occasions 147

Waverley Chuckles 149

CONTENTS

Acknowledgements

During various cruises in 2021 on *Waverley*, I received great assistance for this book from members of the Paddle Steamer Society, *Waverley* officers and engineers. Also fellow passengers, including my companions Alex and Brenda Petrie, and Stuart Wadsworth.

Meet Big Lizzie,
Master of the *Waverley*

EVERY SHIP IS a woman.

So, why shouldn't the *Waverley*'s captain be female? Someone strong and stable at the helm, who would be a leader of men. And so, cometh the hour, cometh the… woman. The *Waverley* had two female mates in the past, but now it was time for a woman to be the master. Our heroine, Big Lizzie, had the privilege of captaining the iconic ship.

Just as many ships belong to a shipping line, Big Lizzie came from a line of relatives involved in public transport of one kind or another, every one of them acquiring the sobriquet 'Big' due to their name, stature and demeanour as self-assured extroverts. The *Waverley* is full of character and now had a captain to match.

Granny Aggie MacDonald was a well-known Glasgow tram conductress in the '40s and '50s, famous for her caustic, wisecracking tongue and ability to deal with drunks, nyaffs, officialdom and uppity citizens.

Granny Aggie's daughter, Big Bella Lamont, who displayed all the characteristics of her mother, served on the Renfrew Ferry for many years before it was discontinued in 1984. When the Renfrew Ferry was moored on the Clyde at Glasgow and became a nightclub (named 'The Ferry'), Bella was the natural choice as bouncer. And now her daughter, Big Lizzie Lamont, has broken the glass ceiling, continuing the proud family tradition of serving the public, this time on the seagoing legend, PS *Waverley*.

Lizzie (so named by her father, who had worked in the Clyde shipyards and had been proud of the ocean-going Cunard Line Queens) was blessed with the instinctive ability to process multiple pieces of information simultaneously, and as such reigned supreme on the wonderful old paddler. Her seamanship proved to be exceptional, especially in side winds and difficult tides, as the old ship is flat bottomed with a limited keel. That, combined with her amazing verbal dexterity, her no-nonsense hands-on approach, plus devastating wit and rambunctious style, set her out as a formidable individual who could be quite a firecracker.

Lizzie was an imposing woman well into her 40s, with an ever-expanding girth and a wibble-wabble rear due to her fondness for sampling the *Waverley*'s excellent fish suppers. One of the reasons she was often referred to as Big Lizzie was due to her enormous bosom, which always seemed to enter a room before she did. That, and her almost six feet stature plus rasping voice, gave her

gravitas as a born leader of men, and earned respect with both crew and (most) passengers alike.

Lizzie became well used to staring into the distance, her steely eyes sizing up the oncoming weather and adjudging other ships' possible movements, while her computer-like brain, augmented by her nautical science degree, computed the appropriate course to take.

A self-assured extrovert, she seemed impervious to any situation involving problem highfalutin passengers, or her crew. The seamen, whether totally conversant in English or not, knew immediately her orders must be obeyed when her authoritative voice rang out. Lizzie did not 'miss and hit the wall' and could use her wisecracking tongue to great effect. The inherent toughness in Captain Lizzie as a master mariner was enhanced by her defiance in the face of bureaucracy, fog, stormy weather and awkward passengers. Members of the crew who fell foul of her orders were soon given a broadside and marooned back in Glasgow.

Captain Lizzie did not suffer drunks (to whom she would say, 'Listen, pal, you're gonnae get whit ah call cirrhosis o' the river.'). Though she herself occasionally had a propensity for a good malt. It was difficult to fool Big Lizzie. As she always said, 'Listen, ah came up the Clyde oan the *Waverley*, no' a bike!'

Lizzie gained much affection among passengers, so much so that in her time as captain she received three proposals of marriage.

None were accepted.

2

Introducing the *Waverley*

PS *Waverley* is the great survivor. An old lady who is truly a national treasure. The people's paddle steamer that has been gracing the sea around the Clyde for many years. A wonderful example of the quality of Clyde-built ships from the bygone days of steam. A vessel of pre-eminent national importance and a great operational asset for tourism in Scotland with her four star Tourist Board Award.

The wonderful *Waverley*, owned by Waverley Steam

Navigation Company, provides passengers with a tranquil, nostalgic experience away from the humdrum and hurly-burly of modern life.

Why the name *Waverley*? It all stems from Sir Walter Scott's first historical novel, *Waverley*, published in 1814. It is interesting to note that the original title of his manuscript was *'Tis Sixty Years Since*, which was appropriate at the time as the storyline is about an Edward Waverley and his adventures during the 1745 Jacobite uprising, approximately 60 years before the book was written. Edward Waverley now features as a figurehead on the ship's fan-vented paddle box. It should also be noted that although 'waverley' means a 'meadow of swaying wood', PS *Waverley* is an extremely stable vessel.

Clyde paddle steamers started way back in 1812 with Henry Bell's *Comet*. Countless have since been built for service locally, in other parts of the UK or in various locations worldwide. With the exception of the *Waverley*, all present-day examples of paddle propulsion can be found only on lakes, rivers or inland waterways. *Waverley* is truly the last seagoing paddle steamer in the world. At the start of the 20th century there were 29 paddle steamers on the River Clyde. Now there is one – *Waverley*.

Sailing on her is a magical experience. There is nothing better than this fine old side-paddled lady winding her nostalgic way in and out of Scotland's sea lochs or around the coastline, providing transport links for both tourists and locals. A trip is an experience from which you will return with a mind awash with colourful memories.

A blast on her steam whistle as she announces that she is leaving a pier, or giving warning to other vessels, makes the hairs on one's neck rise.

She is the last in a long line of pleasure steamers who gave the 'working classes' the opportunity to escape into another world. Sailing 'doon the watter' from Glasgow to various seaside resorts was, and is, a wonderful experience. Indeed, our heroine, Captain Lizzie, remembers going on family trips on this wonderful ship. Little did she know that one day she would be its Master.

Since her preservation in 1975, when she was taken over by the Waverley Steam Navigation Company, it is estimated that over five million passengers have sailed on the *Waverley*. It is not unreasonable to assume that at least that number sailed on her prior to preservation. At present, she carries well over 100,000 passengers annually. On trips, she carries a crew of 25 and up to 915 passengers.

Passengers join the ship by gangways on her sponson (a projection section providing extra storage and stability), or promenade decks where there are fore and aft shelters. Above is the observation deck, accessed by a stairway. The bridge, which includes the wheelhouse with the captain's accommodation behind it, and a chart room, is above the forward lounge. Stairs (companionways) go back down to the main deck.

The boiler and engine room are midships. A souvenir
shop is in a kiosk close to the restaurant aft. There is also
a second bar on the lower deck which is referred to by
some as the 'washing machine bar', as the water level can
run along the portholes.

Gangways are usually placed on the sponson above
the paddle box. However, depending on tides, access
may be directly from the promenade deck. The captain
normally oversees the passengers embarking and

disembarking from the wings of the bridge.

Waverley carries two lifeboats and also has inflatable rafts and buoyant seating.

The prow can only be visited by the crew. It has a steam winch for ropes and the anchor. There is also an auxiliary tiller.

At the forward end of the aft deck shelter is the purser's office where tickets may be purchased or vouchers exchanged.

Behind the deck shelter is a brass plaque commemorating the earlier PS *Waverley* built in 1898, which was sunk by enemy action at Dunkirk in 1940.

Down in the engine room, engineers in white boiler suits maintain a vigilant watch on *Waverley*'s powerhouse, scanning the major dials and awaiting telegraphed instructions from the bridge. The triple expansion steam engines with their pistons and rods go whirling around causing a constant smell of hot oil and steam. The main crank is attached to both paddle wheels which cannot turn independently.

Some passengers sail on this phenomenon from a bygone age to bring back evocative childhood memories, perhaps chinwagging together about the good old days when more than 40 steamers sailed the Clyde, with rival companies racing from pier to pier. Others, to enjoy the enchantment of travelling on an elegant method of transport as its paddles leave a broad carpet of foam trailing astern. Others, to enjoy the sea air from her large open decks, or to use the observation lounges to take in the wonderful scenery during an enjoyable day out, while listening to the ever-helpful commentary. Many are North American visitors taking their vacation in 'Yurrup'. Yes, sailing on the *Waverley* is a truly magical, charming and unique experience.

A sail on this magnificent vessel is a 'must have' experience, made possible by the enthusiasts who saved her from the scrapyard.

3

Master and Commander

THE OVERCAST SKY had cleared. Now it was streaked with gold and red. The air was warm with the familiar smell of the sea. A great golden light drenched the hills, suggesting infinite distances of country beyond the Clyde. Although a thin line of cloud sat on the top of Goat Fell, its various summits were still catching the afternoon sun. All that could be heard was the thump of the paddles, the screeching and squawking of seagulls, and the sound of happy laughter as *Waverley*, with flags flying, pulled away from Brodick pier and the Isle of Arran, into the main channel of her home waters and up the River Clyde.

Lizzie was her usual chirpy self. Today's cruise had gone exceedingly well. The *Waverley* was running like a well-oiled sewing machine.

But that was about to change.

'In the name o' the wee man,' she exclaimed. 'Where did that come from? Is that a submarine on the radar coming up behind us?'

'Aye, captain, looks like it,' replied Chief Officer Dougie. 'They're not submerged, fur ah can see their conning tower.'

With a face that suggested a dire case of constipation, Lizzie said, 'Ah'm fair scunnered wi' they big lumps o' nuclear fission goin' up and doon the Clyde. Right, get the depth charges ready.'

'Whit! This is the *Waverley*, Captain. No' a destroyer.'

'Jist kidding. We'll use missiles instead.'

'Captain Lizzie! Behave yersel. Keep the heid. This is a paddle steamer. Anyway, they're on our side, or should be. And they have about eight small escort boats surrounding them. I think it's two police and six marine ones, no doubt all armed to the teeth.'

'OK. We won't attack. As Ah huvnae even a whizz bang firework, Ah'll jist gae them a dirty look.'

Despite her unusual chutzpah, it was generally voiced abroad that Lizzie was born to be a sea captain, having come out of the womb seemingly knowing port was left and starboard right. She was now regarded as the ideal person to command the throbbing bridge of the *Waverley*.

Just then the radio broke into sound.

'Hey, Captain, ma'am,' said Second Mate Shuggie. 'That's that submarine on the blower and it's an American voice. The cheeky lot are saying we should get this old tub oot the road as they're on important government business, and are late for their scheduled berthing in Loch Long.'

Lizzie went red in the face. Her fingers wagged in

DOUGIE

fury at the armada behind. 'That takes the biscuit. We've nae depth charges and nae guns an' that bit o' kit could wipe us aw aff the face o' the Earth in a jiffy. Right, Shuggie. Whit are we makin' at present?'

'Twelve knots, Captain.'

'Take her up to 15 knots. An' if Chief Engineer Hamish can squeeze anything else oot the pistons, tell him tae let it rip.'

'Aye, aye, Captain,' replied Shuggie, a great smile spreading across his face.

Five minutes later, an American accent was heard on the radio. 'Ahoy, *Waverley*. Listen. We are an ally of yours. We are members of NATO. So slow down and move aside.'

'Jist ignore them,' ordered Lizzie.

The American was heard again. 'Gee, buddy. We are on international business. This nuclear sub cost two billion dollars. We have heavily armed escorting vessels. You're just a tourist ship.'

'Just a tourist ship!' exploded Lizzie. 'Right. Get onto the engine room again and see if we can get up more speed. See Americans and their gung-ho attitude! Just a bunch o' bampots. Ah'll show them. Now, let me speak tae this arrogant wee man in that tin can. Right! Ah'm Master o' the *Waverley*. Who am Ah speaking tae?'

'You are speaking to Commander John Humble of the USS *Abilene*.'

'Well, Commander Humble, may I humbly suggest you may have been on international business, but you're now in oor UK waters. So, jist you listen tae me, Humble,' bellowed Lizzie. 'First of all, I am not your buddy. Your tin can might have cost two billion dollars, but the *Waverley* is priceless. It's no' jist wan o' yer Mississippi showboats, ye know. I am the proud Master of this internationally renowned vessel. We have over 900 passengers on board, many of them your countrymen. So jist you be a nice wee cowboy and follow in oor wake, or submerge if you like and get oot o' ma sight. Nae mair complaints. Dae ye hear? So jist haud yer wheesht!'

A voice was heard. 'We have a problem here. It's a woman, I think, but she sounds like one of those alpha male types who wants to play rough. I cannot understand a word she is saying.'

Everyone on the bridge of the *Waverley* was smiling, clearly enjoying the confrontation.

'Well, madam Captain. So you want to play hardball, eh? Let me tell you what we are about to do. We are going to inform the Pentagon of this situation and get them to contact your government to order you to give us water and let us pass. We need to make high tide at Loch Long.'

'Listen,' retorted Lizzie. 'Rabbie Burns said, "Nae man can tether time nor tide." So, jist you hitch yer wagon onto oor wake, cowboy, and skedaddle up tae yer conning tower, relax and admire oor lovely Scottish scenery.'

So saying, she put down the receiver on its cradle.

'Ah'm no' puttin' up wi' any mair o' this nonsense,'

said Lizzie turning to Chief Officer Dougie and Second Mate Shuggie, her bridge officers. 'Anyway, it's time fur me tae chat' wi' some o' oor passengers.'

Lizzie made her way down onto the deck, smiling and talking to passengers as she went. Chinwagging with customers was one of her delights, the weather and timetable being the usual conversation pieces. And you could meet some very interesting people.

Suddenly she felt a tug on her sleeve. 'Excuse me, Captain,' said an old lady. 'We seem to be going rather fast and do you know there is a submarine directly behind us? Is it Russian? Are we in any danger? What should I do if this ship sinks?'

'Listen, madam, this ship will not sink. The last ship called *Waverley* only sank during the Second World War after the Nazis put umpteen bombs and torpedoes intae her. An' Ah huvnae seen ony o' that lot aroon lately. By the way. Are you married, madam?'

'No, still looking,' the passenger giggled.

'Well, that is an American submarine chasing us. Russian subs have windows so they can spy on us. This Yankie sub wull no doubt be full o' Hollywood Brad Pitt types. So you can have yer pick o' them an' Ah'll maybe get wan as well. Actually, Ah get the impression their captain quite fancies me. Ah can always tell these things. Ah get a wee tingle, ye see. Heaven knows, Ah've been lookin fur a good man fur years.'

'Same here, Captain. But does such a man exist?'

'Well, Ah can tell you, madam, Ah've been oot wi'

hunners in Glesca an' huvnae found wan yet.'

Lizzie went down the companionway to the saloon, ordered chips and tea, then proceeded to munch them

SHUGGIE

while sitting next to a couple of female passengers.

'Enjoying yer cruise, ladies?' she politely asked.

'Yes, Captain. We are finding it quite exciting, and as you are sitting here, we can now tell our friends we were actually dining at the captain's table.'

'Aye, that could be right. Unfortunately, I will not be having a captain's cocktail party.'

'That's a pity, Captain. But why is the *Waverley* fairly racing along? At what time do we reach Dunoon?'

'Oh, in aboot an hour, or even earlier at oor present rate o' knots.'

Just then, Chief Officer Dougie appeared beside them in an obviously agitated state. 'Captain! Captain Lizzie! You'll need to come back to the bridge. The Prime Minister is on the blower.'

'My, my, Captain. That is thrilling,' trilled the two passengers in unison. 'What is the problem?'

'No problem, ladies. Probably just wants to book up for oor next cruise roon Arran,' replied Lizzie with a wink. 'Sorry, I will need to go topside.'

'Right, Chief Officer, lead the way. Ah'm no' too sure Ah really want tae speak tae him, anyways. Efter aw, Ah didnae vote fur him.'

'Whether ye voted fur him or no', Captain Lizzie, he is sounding a bit pit oot.'

'Okay. Give me that receiver. Hullowreer, Prime Minister. How can Ah help ye?' asked Lizzie, while grinning to her bridge officers.

Over the crackling static Lizzie heard, 'Am I speaking

to the most senior person on the Paddle Steamer *Waverley*?'

'That would be me, sur.'

'Madam! Are you trying to cause an international incident? I have just had the President of the United States on my red phone about one of their nuclear submarines. I believe you are obstructing its passage up the River Clyde. Is that correct?'

'Prime Minister, this is the world's last seagoing paddle steamer. Millions of people all over the planet love this special old ship, whereas millions of people are most unhappy with his glorified gunboat.'

'Let me tell you, madam, that if you refuse to give way to this key ally of the United Kingdom, I will be forced to ask the Royal Navy to intervene.'

'Why can't that sub just submerge and go underneath us? Or maybe jist scoot roon aboot us?'

'I am reliably informed, Captain, that there is an agreed limit on speed for submarines in British waters. So, do your duty as a responsible captain and British citizen, and kindly move aside.'

'But then Ah might miss ma timetable and be late getting intae Dunoon, Prime Minister.' And Lizzie winked at the officers on the bridge.

'This is intolerable, Captain. You are leaving me no option.'

'Aye. Whitever ye say yersel, Prime Minister.'

The line went dead and Lizzie turned to the officers on the bridge. 'Yon's wan o' they privileged stuffed shirt twits who talks mince.'

'Well, Captain Lizzie, ye need tae be awfa careful,' cautioned Dougie. 'The marines on the escort boats could board us. Remember first and foremost we have tae take care o' oor passengers. They are of paramount importance, you know.'

'Aye, yer right, Ah suppose,' agreed Lizzie reluctantly.

'Ah jist had a wee rush o' blood tae the heid. Okay. Get that Yank on the blower again.'

'Hullorerr, Submarine Commander Humble.'

'Yes, honey,' came the American accent from the

submarine. 'So, you're now going to let us pass?'

'Aye, maybes, pal. Ah must admit that 'honey' bit certainly gets me going. So, Ah tell ye whit. Here's the deal. You take me oot fur a night in Glesca, plus a nice bunch o' flooers, an' yer oan!'

Everyone on the bridge grinned in astonishment.

There was a moment's silence before the submarine commander exclaimed, 'Wow! Gee-whizz. What I've got to do for Uncle Sam.'

'It's up to you, sunshine. The President wull probably gae ye a medal.'

'Okay, honey. You have a deal. I'm off duty next week.'

'Well, Ah'm workin' on the *Waverley* next week. So jist you come on a cruise oot of Glesca one day. Take your pick which day. We're going to Cumbrae, Largs, Bute, Arran, Mull of Kintyre and the Clyde coast. You can treat me tae a meal on board, and I will even give you a wee shot o' driving a real boat.'

'Sounds like it could be fun. Just as long as we give way to any other subs sailing up your Clyde,' he laughed. 'And you're right by the way, honey. Your Scottish scenery is magnificent.'

'Aye. An' listen, Humble. We haven't met. So, you definitely ain't seen nothin' yet!'

Waverley Chuckles

'Excuse me, Captain
Lizzie,' enquired 'Stoorsooker', the *Waverley*'s Danish
cleaner. 'Me try tae keep the ship spick an' span, but
whit aboot the occasional droppings of seagulls on to
Waverley?'
'Aye,' observed Lizzie with a straight face. 'It's an issue
we cannae dodge.'

'Excuse me, Captain Lizzie,' enquired the elderly gentleman. 'What action do you take if a seagull does its business on the *Waverley's* deck?'
'We've nae poop deck, so we don't let it oan the next cruise, sur.'

'Captain,' said the American passenger, 'recently I was on an Atlantic cruise and we all had great fun with an ice-bucket challenge.'
'Listen, madam. This is the Paddle Steamer *Waverley*. No' the *Titanic*!'

'Excuse me, Captain,' asked the female passenger as she boarded the *Waverley* in Glasgow. 'I feel I should have dressed more appropriately for today's cruise. What do you think?'
'Madam, you look just fine to me. Unless ye want tae go and get yersel a parrot an' a widden leg, an' then entertain us all with a sea shanty.'

'Are you a member of the crew?' asked the tourist.
'Aye. I am Wee Gerry, the Junior Purser.'
'I don't understand a great deal about sailing, Wee Gerry, but what happens when the *Waverley* gets into the doldrums and there is a lack of wind?'
'Well, first of all that really only applied to vessels under sail. And secondly, we have Captain Lizzie in charge, so there is never any lack of wind!'

The *Waverley* was midway between Brodick and Ardrossan.

A particularly nervous passenger asked Lizzie, 'Hypothetically, Captain, if the *Waverley* sank right now and I wanted to swim to the nearest land, how far would that be?'

'About a hundred yards, sur.'

'Amazing. Which way?'

'Down!'

'Hey, Captain,' exclaimed the red-faced, twee, middle-aged man with the trim moustache. 'There are no condom machines in the gents.'

'Listen, pal. This is a paddle steamer. No' the boat o' love.'

The engine order telegraph and bell seemed to be going crazy. It had rung 'Full Astern', 'Full Stop', then 'Half Ahead', confusing Alex, the second engineer.

'In the name o' the wee man,' he exclaimed.

'Does Big Lizzie want this ship to go backwards, furrit, or up or doon?'

The extremely drunk fellow staggered to the foot of the gangway ready to board *Waverley* at Pacific Quay in Glasgow.

Big Lizzie was standing at the foot of the gangway and held up her hand.

'Sorry, sur, but you can't come ontae ma ship in that state.'

'Ah'm jist goin' fur a bleedin' cruise,' the drunk remonstrated. 'Anyways, ur you the heid honcho?'
'Ah am! So, it's like this, sur. You're already three sheets to the wind, so boozers cannae be cruisers. Aff!'

'Captain Lizzie,' observed a passenger. 'A few o' yer passengers seem tae spend quite a long time in the bar.'
'Aye. If you ask me some o' them will be getting cirrhoris o' the river.'

'And did you enjoy our sightseeing trip along the West Coast, madam?' asked Lizzie to an overseas visitor.
'Well, yes. But sometimes your mountains keep getting in the way!'

4

The Wedding

MILLPORT, ON THE Isle of Cumbrae, is one of the most popular resorts on the River Clyde.

Over many years it has been used by numerous Clyde steamers. However, *Waverley* has a distinct advantage over most of them. She is a shallow-draught vessel and has no problem accessing the pier, even at low tide. Steamers using Millport pier mustn't have a draught greater than seven feet.

This is especially important as there are five small, rocky islands just outside the harbour which have to be navigated, and there is little room to manoeuvre.

Despite these hazards, Millport was one of Captain Lizzie's favourite destinations. As a child she spent a week most summers with her granny in a wee flat on the island.

Today was really special. A wedding in the beautiful Cathedral of the Isles on Cumbrae, and the wedding reception to be held on the *Waverley* as she steamed her way back up the Clyde to Glasgow. It was a private hire of the vessel, which was in itself unusual, but the bridegroom had popped the question on the *Waverley* the previous year. Therefore, it seemed only logical that the celebrations take place on the ship. 'If Ah ever get merrit,' thought Lizzie, 'Ah'll have ma reception on the *Waverley*, tae.'

Overnight, *Waverley* had berthed, as usual, at Pacific Quay in Glasgow. Then it was a case of picking up the majority of the one hundred guests, including the bride and her father. All were dressed in their finery for the special day.

Lizzie had made a point of being especially early on board as she wished to welcome everyone personally as they came up the gangway. All of the guests were clearly in high good spirits. The bride was flushed with excitement but her father looked nervous. 'My mother is no longer with us,' she explained, as she introduced her dad. Lizzie gave her father a second look. He was a fine-looking man of around 50 with a full head of hair and an engaging smile.

'I am delighted that my daughter's wedding reception is being held on this wonderful ship, Captain Lizzie.' Then, giving her a smile that made her catch her breath, he shook her hand. 'Such a fine, firm handshake,' she thought. 'Ah fair fancy you, pal.'

A few other guests, including the groom and his best man, plus the famous Scottish folk band, The Wherries, who would be playing at the reception, would come to Cumbrae on the Caledonian MacBrayne ferry from Largs on the Ayrshire coast.

Although just nine o'clock in the morning, the occasional raucous laughter betrayed that some had already entered into the spirit of the day.

Lizzie was excited, too. She just loved a good wedding, and this one was special as she had been asked along to the cathedral as a guest. It had been a while since she had been at such an event and Lizzie had gone a little bit overboard, as she herself put it. A beautiful red suit which clung in all the right places and an arresting hat of red and black, in keeping with the *Waverley*'s colours, had been purchased. Now there was the bride's father to think about. 'Definitely a nice man,' she mused.

The weather outlook was good, blue skies with occasional cloud. Lizzie had made sure that the *Waverley* was well prepared for what promised to be a really special day. The vessel had duly taken on a vast array of food and drink.

With a few cheerful hoots of her horn, *Waverley* set off to cruise down the Clyde to Millport.

Lizzie stood on the bridge eagerly anticipating the day's proceedings. Speed was restricted on the upper part of the Clyde, allowing her plenty of time to admire the familiar passing landscape. *Waverley* sailed on serenely past the old shipbuilding heartland of Glasgow, through Govan, Partick, Scotstoun and then Clydebank where the mighty Cunard Line Queens of the past had been built. People on the banks of the river waved warmly to the popular old vessel or took photos on their mobiles.

From there, the river ran west of Glasgow, past Renfrew and under the huge Erskine Bridge with its thundering traffic.

Dumbarton Rock came into view, along with Ardmore Point sitting between Cardross and Helensburgh. A flotilla of small yachts with colourful spinnakers appeared, apparently involved in a race or regatta, so *Waverley* had to be careful to avoid them. The yachtsmen also waved lovingly at the paddler.

'What a wonderful part of Scotland we live in here in the West of Scotland,' said Lizzie to Chief Officer Dougie. 'Lovely scenery, lovely day, and a wedding. Just perfect.'

Both Lizzie and the *Waverley* were now as one, sailing in a sea of calm expectation.

Lizzie opted to go down onto the deck and was immediately approached by one of the male guests. A good-looking individual with excellent teeth who seemed determined to take up all of her time and was continually in Lizzie's face. He seemed particularly interested in the layout of the vessel. Lizzie was keen to further ensure that everything was shipshape, and was getting a bit fed up with his persistent questions.

'So, tell me Captain, where do you sleep aboard the *Waverley*?'

'Ah've got a cabin at the back o' the bridge,' she informed him, before adding abruptly, 'An' let me tell you, pal, you've nae chance!'

'But listen, Captain Lizzie, you don't know what you

will be missing. When I kiss a woman she really knows she's been kissed.'

'Is that so. Who tells her?'

She moved away quickly leaving the man open-mouthed.'

On the south side of the river, the *Waverley* passed close to Port Glasgow, then it was on past the whale-like wreck of the sugar boat MV *Captayannis* on a sandbar just off the town of Greenock, where it had lain since a storm in 1974.

This meant they were now at the Tail of the Bank, the deep water anchorage in the upper Firth of the Clyde, the Clyde at this point in its course being wide, deep and flowing energetically.

Soon they had passed the town of Gourock with the Cloch Lighthouse nearby. Then Dunoon, and Largs could be seen before *Waverley* approached the Isle of Cumbrae, and their destination of the town of Millport.

The pier at Millport always made Lizzie smile. It was the only one she knew of where the planks were all numbered so that they could be assembled correctly after a severe storm. Something like painting with numbers, she always thought.

Once *Waverley* was made secure, a gangway from the sponson cover over the paddle box allowed the guests to disembark. A waiting coach would shuttle them over to the small cathedral a mile and a half away. The bride, Norma McAleese, soon to be Mrs Jack Anderson, along with her father, would remain on the

Waverley for a further half hour until it was time for them to set off by limo for the cathedral.

Lizzie walked around *Waverley*, making a thorough inspection of all the preparations before leaving her beloved ship in the capable hands of Chief Officer Dougie.

The coach had now returned from the cathedral after delivering its first group of guests, and so Lizzie joined the remaining guests. The vehicle drove along the seafront of Millport, past the distinctive crocodile rock with its gaping mouth, which was being inspected by a group of day-trippers.

The coach turned inland, up College Street, before stopping at the main gates of Britain's smallest cathedral.

The remaining guests, along with Lizzie, entered its driveway, before climbing up a flight of worn stone steps to the tall, impressive building. Lizzie could hear wedding music and quite suddenly felt emotional.

Lizzie entered through a well-weathered wooden door. Then onto a floor of flagstones which echoed with the clip-clop of stilettos, as ushers led everyone to their seats.

Lizzie was seated on an aisle pew just three rows back from the principal guests. When the organist started to play 'Here Comes the Bride' she immediately thought on words from her childhood: 'Here comes the bride, 50 inches wide, sailing doon the aisle, like a steamer oan the Clyde.' Then she had a terrible thought.

'Heavens, Ah wid noo be much mair than 50 inches!'

Lizzie looked around at the assembled group of relations and friends of the pair. The women with slight smiles on their faces, occasionally wiping away a tear. The men keen for the formalities to be over so they could perhaps get to the bar on the ship.

The ceremony duly began with the minister, a cheery, fatherly fellow, announcing, 'Dearly beloved, I am the Very Reverend Stuart, the minister of this lovely Cathedral of the Isles. I am aware that most of you have arrived here on the famous old paddler, *Waverley*. Well, like the *Waverley*, this cathedral has a captain, and that is me. So, I will hopefully direct the happy couple through today's ceremony, and pray that they themselves can steer through the sometimes stormy seas of marriage.'

The ceremony then got under way, and soon came to the inevitable, nerve-racking question put to everyone present at weddings. Thankfully, after an anxious moment, there was silence. Then it was time to exchange rings. Lizzie had a great view of the couple and couldn't help noticing that the groom had a glaikit look on his face. 'Probably he's been in a pub in Largs before catching the ferry over,' she thought. The bride had clearly recognised that her future husband was somewhat tipsy, and for a minute it looked as though they might exchange blows never mind rings. A few choice Anglo-Saxon epithets in his ear quickly seemed to get him back on track.

Lizzie enjoyed the wedding ceremony, especially two parts of it. Firstly, when the bride's father gave her away. 'Lovely lookin' fellow,' she thought. 'Might get a dance wi' him on the way back tae Glesca.' And then when the minister pronounced them man and wife, and the small page boy turned around, and in a loud voice asked, 'Mummy, can he give her the seed now?'

Soon it was the turn of the photographer outside the cathedral, before the guests were transported the short distance back to the waiting *Waverley*.

The weather had remained warm and sunny. The bride and groom lined up on deck at the top of the gangway and welcomed everyone on board to their reception. Tables of champagne and canapes had been set up and soon everyone was chatting and laughing, with the decibels increasing in proportion to the alcohol consumption. Eventually, the best man succeeded in getting everyone's attention to announce that the meal would be served downstairs after the *Waverley* set sail.

With a few loud blasts from the old paddler the stern lines were let go. The happy wedding party waved goodbye to the well-wishers on the harbourside, and off they set, at minimum speed, to meander back up the River Clyde to Glasgow.

It was when the *Waverley* was off Rothesay Bay that the shout came up to the bridge. 'Captain! We have a problem.' It was Shuggie, the second mate, who was standing beside a man apparently under the influence.

Lizzie came down onto the deck. 'So, what's the

problem, Shuggie?'

'Captain. We have a stowaway. It's this fellow,' he said, pointing to a red-faced older man beside him.

'Are you a guest at this wedding ?' Lizzie asked somewhat curtly.

'Naw me, hen,' he slurred. 'Ah'm jist here fur a wee sail. Ye see it's an awfa nice day an' Ah jis thought Ah'll get masel oan the *Waverley*.'

'Where dae you live?'

'Ah live in Millport, of course. Ye see Ah wis in Frasers fur a wee drinkypoo, and Ah saw the *Waverley* sittin' there, so Ah says tae masel, Ah'll jist go fur a wee sail, ye ken.'

'This is a private hire today. We don't stop until we get back to Glasgow.'

His mouth dropped. 'Whit am Ah gonnae do?'

'Dae you live with someone in Millport?'

'Aye. Ma trouble-an'-strife. She'll kill me.'

'Ah wid kill ye, tae,' responded Lizzie, 'if you were mine.'

'Whit's yer name an' address an' we'll let the police in Millport know, an' they can tell your wife whit has happened and that you won't be home till tomorrow. We'll be back in at Millport on our normal schedule tomorrow, so you can sleep on board tonight.'

'Aw. That's right kind o' ye, hen. Ma name's Wullie Smith. But listen, if the polis turns up at oor door the wife'll think Ah've drapped deid.'

'She might actually be disappointed when she finds out what's really happened to you!' retorted Lizzie.

'You're gey sozzled, so jist you sit up at the bow away frae the wedding guests.'

'Ah'm real sorry aboot this, hen. Ah don't want tae spoil the big day fur the happy couple.'

'Aye, well. Ah jist hope they're still happy. An' ye'll make me happy if you don't call me hen again. Ah'm the captain an' Ah'm no' chicken. Dae ye hear?'

'Sorry, missus. Er, sorry, Captain.'

Back on the bridge, Lizzie scanned the horizon. There was very little traffic apart from a couple of container ships and a ferry. The river remained calm and peaceful, just the way she liked it. Then she heard raised voices and, looking down, saw that it was the newlyweds apparently having a rammy. A few guests plus the photographer had gathered around them on deck for the cutting of the bridal cake which lay on a small table by the rails. The row seemed to be intensifying when suddenly the bride, with a few well-chosen words, grabbed the base of the cake and with one almighty heave threw it over the side.

There was a stunned silence. All that could be heard was the turning of the paddles. Then a shout went up. 'Ah'll get it fur ye, darlin'!' Followed by the vision of Wullie the stowaway perched on the sponson, before launching himself into the frothing sea.

'Telegraph stop!' shouted Lizzie. 'Then get her intae reverse, heap pronto. Let's get this bampot back on board. Ah hope he can swim.'

Waverley was now in reverse with everyone on board

conscious of the change in direction. Lizzie saw the man
in the water a couple of hundred yards behind. 'Slowly
does it now,' she instructed. 'Not too near this numpty.'
Waverley duly edged up beside the splashing stowaway.
A life belt was thrown to the drunk, who was somehow
managing to hold aloft what looked like half of one of
the wedding cake tiers. He was unceremoniously pulled
aboard onto the lower deck before being half dragged
up to face Lizzie. He stood on thin spindle shanks,
quivering and shaking with cold, clearly sobering up as

he realised the seriousness of the situation.

'Right, you!' shouted Lizzie, standing in front of him with bosom all a quiver. 'Whit dae ye think you are playing at? You have endangered my ship and upset a wedding party. Ah have a good mind to place you in irons until we get back to Glasgow and then hand you over to the police.'

'No, no, Captain Lizzie.' Lizzie looked around and there were the bride and groom, arms around each other. 'It was our stupid fault. What a daft thing to do, throwing our cake overboard. Please forgive us, Captain Lizzie, and please forgive this poor man. He nearly gave his life to rescue oor wedding cake. In fact,' continued the bride, looking lovingly at her new husband, 'he has rescued oor marriage. Efter aw, it wis jist a wee lover's tiff. We were a wee bit impulsive ye see, what wi' the champagne an' aw that.' And the bride leaned over and gave Wullie a kiss on his silly, grinning face.

They looked pleadingly at Lizzie.

'Okay. Get Wullie doon tae the engine room an' dry him out,' ordered Lizzie to Big Gerry, the purser.

'Great,' said the groom. 'Thanks fur yer understandin, Captain Lizzie. 'Wance he's a bit dryer he can maybe be a special guest at the top table.'

'Well, it's your wedding, your choice, your funeral, sunshine,' replied Lizzie with her fists clenched, still clearly annoyed. 'But Ah'm gonnae huvtae pit this incident in the ship's log. *Waverley* is a wee bit limited when it comes tae tight turns, so we had to paddle backwards, which Ah don't like, tae get tae him oan time before he drowned.'

'We are awfa sorry, Captain Lizzie. But Ah think we might actually adopt Wullie as an uncle. Look, he has even given us oor wedding cake back. Well, a wee bit of it,' said the bride, holding up a still dripping lump of cake. 'We're gonnae keep this as a souvenir o' oor waddin.'

'Well, we're certainly no' goannae eat it,' grinned the groom.

'Okay,' said Lizzie, taking command of the situation. 'But we need tae get the ship moving again. Chief Officer Dougie, please get her under way.'

But on her way back to the bridge Lizzie heard another scream, this time coming from below deck. Looking down the stairwell she saw Second Engineer Alex with a young lady in his arms.

'And jist whit are you playing at, Alex?'

Getting no answer she went down the stairs and confronted the dark-haired young woman.

'Is this man annoying you, miss?'

'No, certainly not, Captain. I tripped on these stairs, which I may add are quite steep, and I seemed to go flying but this kind man appeared out of the blue and caught me.'

Lizzie looked directly at Alex. 'So you just go around catching damsels in distress, do you? Well, as the young lady in question appears to be okay, can I suggest that you get back to your duties.'

'Yes, Captain. But I was just helping Brenda, you understand.'

'Brenda, is it? By golly you're a quick worker, sunshine.'

'Right, Captain,' replied Alex as he went on his way with one last longing look at the girl.

'Glad you're okay, miss,' said Lizzie. 'You've just got to be careful on these steps with high heels.'

It was not long afterwards that the wedding dinner began. It was a help yourself job, and as Lizzie was filling her plate she sort of accidentally bumped against the bride's father.

He turned and looked at her and said, 'For a minute I thought you were going to get Wullie to walk the plank, Captain.'

'Well, he had already sort of done that. Och, Ah suppose the auld soul really meant well. Anyway, today's supposed to be a happy occasion.'

'The trouble is my daughter is bit quick tempered, just like her late mother.'

'Oh, right. So you're a widower, then.'

'Yes, at present I am. But I've now got my eye on a wee lady who is actually one of the bridesmaids today. That is, if she will have me.'

Lizzie thought, 'Well, Ah wid hae ye. Heavens, Ah've jist nae luck wi' men whitsoever.'

'Oh, right. Ah hope it works out for you,' Lizzie replied, trying to hide her disappointment.

'Anyways, Captain Lizzie, maybe we could have wee dance later on. And I can tell everyone I had a dance with the master of the famous *Waverley*.'

So it transpired that Lizzie did dance around the deck. The wedding guests were clearly enjoying the popular music of The Wherries and so did she. As she was swept along she couldn't help but notice that the bride and Wullie the stowaway were also dancing. 'By heavens,' she thought, 'he's havin' a day an' a half o' it.'

It was getting on towards midnight as the *Waverley* once more sailed serenely under the Erskine Bridge. As Lizzie walked the decks doing her final rounds, she heard various guests saying that it had been the best wedding ever. Certainly, it had been eventful.

Once *Waverley* was tied up at Pacific Quay, Lizzie stood at the bottom of the gangway saying farewell to all the guests. Suddenly she noticed Wullie sneaking down in the middle of a group of people. She immediately stood astride the gangway. 'And where dae ye think you're going, sunshine? You're not leaving this ship until we get back tae Millport tomorrow. Dae ye hear?'

'Sorry, Captain. Ah wis jist going fur a wee stroll.'

'Aye. An' just look whit happened when ye went on a wee stroll ontae this ship. Go an' see Big Gerry the purser an' he wull get ye a space to sleep in the crew mess room.'

Next down the gangway came Alex, the second engineer, along with Brenda, the lady he had prevented falling down a stairwell.

'My, my,' exclaimed Lizzie. 'This really has turned out a bit of a love-boat today.'

'Oh, yes, Captain,' said the starry-eyed girl, 'Alex and I are getting on just a treat.'

Alex blushed and nodded his head.

'That's all very well,' said Lizzie. 'But remember, Alex, you are to be back on board by seven tomorrow morning.'

'Aye, skipper. Ah'll remember.'

And off they went, rather close together.

Then the newlyweds, arms entwined, also made their way off the *Waverley*. Lizzie wished them all the luck in the world.

'Wonderful day, Captain Lizzie. We'll never forget you or the *Waverley*. Any good advice, Captain, you know, for oor marriage?' the bride shyly asked Lizzie.

'Well, ma advice to you is the same as Noah gave to his passengers as they disembarked aff his ark. Go forth and multiply!'

Waverley Chuckles

Coming down the companionway, Lizzie slipped and
tumbled to the bottom.
'Excuse me, Captain Lizzie,' inquired Wee Gerry, the
junior purser, 'Did you miss a step?'
'Naw,' replied Lizzie. 'Ah hit every wan o' them!'

It had been quite a long day. As usual, Captain Lizzie
had made a point of mixing and conversing with
passengers whenever possible. Each time she walked
up the port side deck two miserable older women
sitting there followed her every move. Lizzie's cheery
'Hullowrerr, ladies' failed to raise a response.
As *Waverley* was nearing the end of her cruise, Lizzie
was doing her final walkabout of the day. As she
passed the glassy-eyed pair she just couldn't resist it.
'Wull Cinders be waitin' fur ye at Pacific Quay?'

Lizzie was socialising with an older gentleman tourist
in the saloon. 'Perhaps Ah could offer ye a wee
refreshment,' she asked.
'That would be most kind of you, Captain. Could I have
a pint of heavy with some lemonade and lime in it?'
'Ah'm awfa sorry, sur. But we don't do cocktails on the
Waverley. Jist kiddin!'

'Captain, Captain, I think that I have just seen a shark,'
exclaimed the excited female passenger.
'Aye, madam. We do have various types of sharks in
Scottish waters.'
'Well, this one, Captain, had a huge open mouth as
though it was looking for food or even money.'
'Och, yes. That would be a busking shark, madam.'

The young, well-muscled man stopped Lizzie as she waddled round the deck.

'Hey, Captain. Dae ye have a gym on this ship?'

'Aye,' she laughed. 'Knowin' him he's probably having a sly fag up at the prow.'

Lizzie was called to go down to the saloon as there apparently was a potential problem with a 'wee Glesca hard man'.

She discovered a small man remonstrating with the staff.

'So,' he said in an aggressive voice, 'Ur you the captain o' this boat?'

'Aye. An' Ah hear you think you're a wee Glasgow hard man?'

'Ah'll have you know Ah wis born in a cement mixer.'

'Well, sunshine, if you're a wee hard man that wis brought up in a cement mixer it is reasonable to assume you won't float.'

'Whit dae ye mean?'

'Ah'm the law on this vessel. So, it's two o' sand an' wan o' cement and over the side fur you.'

'Oh, haud oan. Ah wis jist at the kiddin'.'

'Well, Ah'm no' at the kiddin'. You're aff at the next stop which is Campbeltown.'

'An' how am Ah expected tae get back tae Glesca fae there?'

'Maybes you could get a lift oan a cement mixer, sunshine!'

'So, you are the lady captain on this vessel,' smiled the American woman tourist. 'May I ask you a question I have often pondered? Do Scotsmen wear anything under their kilt?'
'Ah'm very sorry, madam, but I couldn't possibly say. However, you will notice that Ah have a big smile on ma face.'

The members of the Light Opera Company were giving an impromptu performance of *HMS Pinafore* to passengers on the forward deck.
The trouble was that the vessel was almost in at Rothesay harbour, but due to the number of passengers assembled forward, a crew member had failed to gain enough space to swing the line onto the pier.
Lizzie saw the problem and shouted down from the bridge, 'Hey! Stand back. We are trying tae tie up.'
A voice was heard from the Light Opera Company.
'But, Captain, we were just singing about the captain of HMS *Pinafore*.'
'Aye, well. Ah'm the captain of the PS *Waverley*. No' a kiddie-oan wan. So, move!'

'Captain, I must say, Scotland is beautiful,' enthused the Australian tourist. 'All these lochs we have gone through are just fantastic. But perhaps you could answer a question? Why does Scotland have so many hills and mountains?'

'Well, it's like this, madam. Ye see the Scots have been winning so much land from the English over the centuries that we had to pile it up somewhere.'

Waverley was running 15 minutes behind schedule. Big Lizzie was on the bridge and it was clear from her expression she was most unhappy.
'Who died, Captain?' asked Second Mate Shuggie.
'Ah huvnae decided yet!'

The overbearing lady from Texas asked Big Lizzie, 'Captain, I don't know a great deal about your country, but have any really big men ever been born here?'
'Naw, madam. Jist wee weans.'

5

Off to Tighnabruaich

LIZZIE PARKED HER car at Pacific Quay, Glasgow. As she got out of the car she could see the impressive outline of *Waverley* berthed nearby.

However, her car was not so impressive and had seen better days. It was an ancient Ford, weatherbeaten and scarred, with rusty sills. Getting to be an old warhorse, something like its owner, but affectionately known as Wee Bella, as she had bought it in the Glasgow district of Bellahouston. Alex, the second engineer on the *Waverley*, gave the car the once-over now and again in order to keep it going, enabling it to stagger through its MOT.

From her parking spot it was only five minutes or so to the dock. Today's cruise was to Rothesay and Tighnabruaich. Not over long, but one of Lizzie's favourites, with an hour's stop in both places. And it looked as though the cruise was fully booked.

Tighnabruaich is a pretty little village situated on the shoreline of the west coast of Loch Fyne on the Kyles of Bute. Tucked away on the southwest of the Cowal

Peninsula in Argyll, it looks across at the north part of the lovely Isle of Bute. The name Tighnabruaich means 'House on the Hill', and there are certainly a number of houses on the hill above the village's old Victorian pier.

Sure enough, the popular paddle steamer was indeed full, and Lizzie just loved when she could hear happy laughter and the excited chatter of passengers.

Once she was satisfied that all was under control, she opted to have a walk around the ship, carefully checking everywhere and everything. Then, back on the bridge, she gave the order to cast off and swing the ship around.

Once under way, Lizzie moved among the crowd and, as usual, was asked to participate in a number of selfies with passengers. Having your photo taken with the captain of the prestigious *Waverley* was popular, and Lizzie enjoyed a wee chat at the same time with the tourists.

'A wee beet windy today, Captain,' observed an elderly European gentleman.

'Och, it's just a bit breezy,' replied Lizzie.

'Well, I saw a seagull flying past, and it was going backwards.'

'Och. Oor seagulls here on the Clyde are all jist showoffs, sur,' she countered with a grin.

Waverley sailed along until she reached the Firth of Clyde, before turning to starboard past Innellan and Toward point, and then she bypassed Rothesay, where she would berth later on in the day. Then it was on through the Kyles of Bute, past the famous painted Lads of Kyle stones on one side, and the painted Lassies of Bute stones on the other, and on towards her first port of call, Tighnabruaich.

Before coming to Tighnabruaich, they passed the small town of Port Driseach, and Lizzie was puzzled when she saw the Tighnabruaich lifeboat sitting alongside a large yacht. 'That's funny,' she thought. 'It's relatively calm today, barely a force three with very little swell.'

Ten minutes later they approached Tighnabruaich pier. As usual, there was a crowd standing on the shoreline to greet the popular paddler.

Various small yachts and vessels bobbed around on their buoys in the bay, making the area even more attractive. Not far away, the lifeboat station stood empty. Only its floating pontoon was there, along with the launching tractor on the slipway. Lizzie had once paid a visit to the lifeboat station, and chatted with the friendly volunteers in the crew room upstairs in the boathouse, before admiring the lifeboat, named *James and Helen Mason*.

There at the pier was Angus, the faithful *Waverley* enthusiast, who always helped to tie her up, and knew everything that was going on in the small village.

'Hey, Angus,' shouted Lizzie from the bridge, 'the lifeboat been away long?'

'It went away a couple of hours ago, Captain Lizzie.'

Lizzie's nose was bothering her, and so, once the *Waverley* was securely berthed and the engines left ticking over, she set off along the road the quarter mile to the lifeboat station.

'So, why's the lifeboat round at Port Driseach, folks?' she asked the couple of people standing around at the station.

'She's away round to Driseach trying to help a big yacht that's stuck on the shore,' explained one. 'Peter the Helm has just been on the radio. They're having difficulty moving her, and the owner of the boat is not over-happy. Hold on, Lizzie, that will be Peter on the blower again.'

'Peter. How's it going? We've got Captain Lizzie here. As you know, *Waverley* is in at the moment. Lizzie, Peter wants to speak to you.'

'Lizzie, Peter here. It's a yacht called *Alotawoman*. And let me tell you, her owner is a lot of woman! We're having difficulty getting this yacht free. To tell you the truth, Ah've never seen a yacht with so much equipment on board. Any chance of the *Waverley* pulling this thing off using your capstan? Wouldn't take you long while you're on your way back down to Rothesay.'

'Mmmm. Well, a wee bit irregular as you know, Peter, especially with passengers on board. Tell you what. We'll do it. I'll tell our passengers that they are just about to witness us helping our friends in the RNLI. In fact, we could maybe have a collection on board for your lifeboat station. You know, sort of pass the hat around.'

'Great idea. That would be smashing. So, when will you be here?'

'I'll need to keep to our timetable as many of our passengers are off having a stroll around Tighnabruaich. We could probably be with you in about three quarters of an hour. The tide is on the rise so that should help.'

'Okay, Lizzie. I'll tell this woman that help is on the way. She is driving me crazy, standing on her deck with fists tightly clenched and a high pitched, ungrateful voice, giving everybody laldy.'

Later, once Lizzie was told that the headcount check was complete and everyone back on board, she gave instructions for the *Waverley* to cast off. Dougie telegraphed the engine room to go half ahead and the ship sailed slowly along the coast to Port Driseach.

It wasn't long before they could see the lifeboat alongside a huge yacht. Lizzie immediately made an announcement over the tannoy.

'Ladies and Gentleman, we are delighted to tell you that *Waverley* is just about to assist our dear friends in the Royal National Lifeboat Institution by helping them pull a yacht off the beach here. There is absolutely no danger to anyone, but please do not all crowd onto the port side decks. So spread out, please. We estimate this will take approximately ten minutes and we will still get to Rothesay on schedule. Thank you.'

The lifeboat came out alongside the *Waverley* and then proceeded to carry a line attached to a mooring rope over to the yacht. Then strong rope was pulled over from the ship and attached to the yacht. Once a shout was heard confirming it was duly attached, Hee-Haw the Donkeyman started the capstan engine. When the tension was tight, Lizzie ordered the ship into reverse. The result was that the yacht slowly slid off the shore as planned, much to the delight and cheers of *Waverley*'s passengers.

'Well, that wis nae bother,' observed Chief Officer Dougie. The rope was then duly recovered and *Waverley* got ready to set off for Rothesay.

But just then, the lifeboat sped out to the ship. Peter the Helm shouted up to the bridge, 'Well done, *Waverley*. The lady who owns this yacht has asked if she could get a lift back to Glasgow. Her crew will look after the yacht.'

Lizzie looked down and there was the woman, hair immaculately done and clearly in the best of yachting gear. 'Jist whit Ah need,' she thought. 'Some posh wummin who talks wi' bools in her mooth who wull no doubt be looking fur first class attention.'

'Aye, okay,' she shouted back reluctantly.

The woman in question was duly assisted, with some difficulty, onto the ship. Lizzie decided to ignore her and instead announced that there would be a collection for the RNLI.

The trip to Rothesay was uneventful, with a volunteer from Waverley Excursions giving the usual helpful commentary to passengers, describing the various features on both sides of the Kyles of Bute.

Rothesay is the main town on the Isle of Bute. Back in Victorian times, it was a fashionable holiday resort. Throughout the years it has remained popular, especially with Glaswegians during the '50s and '60s. It has an impressive, fashionable esplanade lined with palm trees and, of all things, a world-renowned Victorian toilet.

Once berthed in Rothesay, Wee Gerry, the junior purser, came to the bridge to announce that over £2,000 had been raised for the Tighnabruaich lifeboat station.

'An' Ah bet ye that wumin didnae put in a penny,'

Lizzie declared.

'Aye, yer right, Captain. Nut a penny.'

'Oh, right. Maybe Ah should go an see this lady sailor. She's startin' tae annoy me!'

The lady in question was found in the saloon chatting to some passengers.

Lizzie introduced herself. 'Hello. Ah'm Captain Lizzie, the master oan this vessel. Pleased we could help. Dae you live in Scotland or down south?'

'Ah'm Maizie McDuff,' came the reply, 'Pleased tae meet ye. An' Ah cumfae Glesca,' was the unexpected response. 'Thanks fur aw yer help, an' fur gaein' me a lift back, Lizzie."

'Oh,' replied a surprised Lizzie. 'Ah didnae expect ye tae speak fluent Glaswegian.'

'Aye. Born an' bred there, so Ah um. Tell ye whit Ah'm tryin' tae dae noo. Ah know it's a bit o' a cheek, but could Ah bum a lift when the ship gets back intae Glesca? Huv you goat a car there, Lizzie? Ah wid get a taxi but Ah've nae money wi' me.'

'Aye, well, okay,' replied an unsure Lizzie. 'But where dae ye live?'

'The best place in Glesca. The People's Republic o' Partick.'

'Fine, nae bother,' Lizzie replied, still somewhat reluctantly. 'Mind you, Ah have tae make sure everything is left shipshape, so tae speak, afore Ah leave the vessel.'

'Nae bother. Ah'm no' in that big a hurry.'

Lizzie turned away. 'Jings. Saved her yacht, gae'd her a lift up the river, an' noo she wants ma tae take her hame. That wan wouldnae gae ye the fuzz aff a peach. Damn cheek, if you ask me.'

Lizzie didn't cast eyes on Maizie again until *Waverley* was back at Glasgow and securely tied up at the quayside. Soon all of the passengers and crew were accounted for and the ship was being cleaned and restocked for the following day's cruise.

And sure enough, there was Maizie waiting for her at the head of the gangway.

'Ma caur is jist over there,' said Lizzie, pointing towards the car park.

Once in the car, Lizzie asked, 'So wull ye go back doon tae Tighnabruaich fur yer yacht wance it's repaired?'

'Naw. Naw. It wull go back tae its mooring at Kip Marina in Inverkip. That's where we goat it. Ah've three boys an' they act as crew. Ye see, they just love the yacht. Jist a pity the bampots ran it aground the day.'

'Aye, right,' replied a somewhat tired and subdued Lizzie.

'Okay, this is where Ah stay,' exclaimed Maizie. 'Hame's best is whit Ah say.' Lizzie stopped her car outside a large tenement building.

As Maizie got out of the car, she smiled and said, 'Thanks again, Captain. Yer a real pal.'

'Aye, right,' replied Lizzie. 'Nae bother.' And then, as she drove off, thought that the woman had been nothing else but bother.

Lizzie was now off duty for six days and could relax. Another captain would be master on the *Waverley* for the following week.

It was just three days later that she received the phone call from the chairman of Waverley Excursions.

'An' jist what were you playing at, Captain,' came a stern voice, 'using the *Waverley* to recover a stranded yacht? Your business is to provide pleasure cruises and look after the safety and welfare of your passengers!'

'Well, Ah wis jist helpin' the Tighnabruaich Lifeboat lot. An' aw the passengers enjoyed it.'

'Well, maybe so, Captain Lizzie. Let me tell you, normally this would be a verbal warning. Never ever do such a thing again. Do you understand?'

'Aye, okay.'

'However, Captain Lizzie, some good has come of all of this. Mrs McDuff has kindly donated half a million pounds to us. In addition, I believe she has also given £100,000 to the Tighnabruaich Lifeboat Station.

'Wow! Heaven's above! Did she win the Lottery or something?'

'Certainly did. Didn't you notice the name of her yacht? It's called the *Alotawoman*. She's the Glasgow woman who won £106 million on the European lottery. So, off the record, Lizzie, well done. In fact, extremely well done!'

'Thanks,' replied a shocked Lizzie.

It took Lizzie quite a time and a number of whiskies

for the information to sink in.

The following week, when Lizzie drove down to start her duty, she parked her car in its usual position. She couldn't help but notice that in the next parking bay was a red BMW with a large ribbon around it, and a note stuck on the bonnet. She just *had* to look.

It said: 'Thanks, Captain Lizzie. Fur heaven's sake get rid o' that auld car o' yours an' keep this wan!'

But she didn't.

Lizzie sold the BMW and distributed the money around the crew. And she held on to Wee Bella. After all, she reasoned, it's really a lovely old thing. Just like the *Waverley*.

Waverley Chuckles

Lizzie was being her usual hospitable self, chatting to a group of men on the deck. One chap told her that they were all dentists, and this was a special day out for their practice.

'That's interesting,' said Lizzie. 'But I think you should know this is the Paddle Steamer *Waverley*, no' the tooth ferry!'

'So, you ur the Captain o' the *Waverley*?' slurred the drunk, looking Lizzie up and down. 'Have ye ever been mistaken fur a man?'
'Naw. Have you?'

'Captain, you must have a lot of responsibilities on this vessel?' observed the paddle steamer enthusiast.
'Yer right. Ah've got tae keep ma eye on the ball, an' then keep my ear to the ground, apart from keeping my shoulder to the wheel. Sometimes Ah feel like a contortionist.'

'Two women sitting on the deck got talking. 'Aye. Ah'm a regular on the *Waverley*. Grand old boat. An' Ah jist love their captain. But by golly, she's a big wummin.'
'Yer right. Probably at least four feet.'
'Four feet?'
'Aye. Lyin' doon!'

The lady had taken up a lot of Lizzie's time. Finally, the woman asked. 'Have I told you yet about my grandchildren, Captain?'
'Naw, an' thank you very much.'

'Captain, a few of your crew clearly come from various countries. Diversity is good. But do you also respect age?' asked the passenger.
'Ah certainly do. Especially when it's bottled.'

'I am led to believe that you are the captain of this vessel,' said the obviously angry, well-dressed older lady.
'I am indeed, madam. How can I help you?'
'It's not a question of just helping me. It's also helping

all of your female passengers.'
'Oh. How can Ah do that, madam?'
'Fix the queuing problem at the ladies toilet. It's not good enough, Captain.'
'Well, it depends on how many women we have on board. Ah call it the 'Aw Needin' Line'.

Lizzie was chatting to an expat who was on board.
'Yes, Captain. Ah used tae stay in Glesca, and then me an' ma husband emigrated to Santa Fe.'
'Oh. Where's Santa Fe?'
'The North Pole! See, Ah huvnae lost ma Glesca sense o' humour, Captain.'

Wee Gerry, the junior purser, asked a passenger who was wanting to purchase yet another ticket:
'Excuse me, sir. In Glasgow you bought a single ticket to Greenock. Then in Greenock you bought a single ticket to Helensburgh. Then at Helensburgh you bought a single ticket to Kilcreggan. At Kilcreggan you bought a single ticket to Rothesay. Why not just buy a ticket to Rothesay in the first place?'
'Well, it's like this, son,' replied the elderly man. 'My specialist says my heart is weak and I could drop at any time. So, you see, I'm only booking from place to place.'

The guy was a pain. He would not stop pestering Lizzie with inane questions. Finally, he asked, 'Captain, what

are the qualities required to be the master of such a prestigious icon as the *Waverley*?'
'Well,' replied Lizzie, 'I would probably say optimism, self-esteem, an outgoing nature, and the ability to cope under stress caused by bampots!'

'Can the *Waverley* cope with very stormy weather, Captain?
'Och, aye. Nae bother. As the auld sailors used to say, 'We might not be able to direct the wind but we can always adjust the sails.' A smooth sea never makes a skilled mariner, you know. And as we are up an' doon the Clyde maist of the time, we have had plenty o' experience.'

Lizzie was chatting to a nice wee family consisting of mum, dad, wee girl and babe in arms.
Lizzie smiled and asked the little girl how old she was. Four was the answer.
'And how old is your little baby brother?'
'Oh, he's too wee. He doesnae even have a number yet.'

Lizzie came across a man jogging up and down the deck, despite the extremely hot weather.
'Excuse me, sur. Ye can promenade a wee bit oan the *Waverley* but she's no' really designed fur running.'
'Sorry, Captain. But ye see Ah've a slipped disc problem. Ah need tae exercise twice a day.'

'Aye, well. Tell ye whit. We'll be in Kilcreggan soon, and as it's a warm day, ye can run up tae the café at the tap of the pier an' get me an ice cream cone. Ye might even fancy wan yersel.'

Two ladies were sheltering at the funnel, keeping out of the wind.
One lady observed, 'Ma auld granny used tae say, *may the wind at your back always be yours.*'
'Aye, well, the trouble wi' ma man in bed is that the wind at ma back is usually his.'

Th high-energy American tourist was clearly tipsy. Her hysterical laughter could be heard way above the noises of the happy guests on board. Furthermore, she would not leave Lizzie's side as the *Waverley*'s captain made her way around the vessel.
Finally, Lizzie asked what her name was. 'Mrs T. Vanderbelt the Second,' was the slurred reply.
'And may Ah ask what the 'T' stands for?'
'Yeah. It stands for Tuesday.'
'Well, it's just a pity your parents hadn't called it a day before then.'
'That's a little rude, Captain. I will have you know we are doing a European tour to celebrate my daughter's coming out.'
'Oh,' replied Lizzie. 'What did she do, and how long wis she in for?'

6

A Whale of a Time

IT WAS THE first week in June, and Lizzie was seated on a bench on the promenade at Largs. She was enjoying an ice cream just purchased from Nardini's.

It was a Sunday, the weather was pleasant, and she looked out across the sea to the Isle of Cumbrae. To her left was the pier where the *Waverley* lay ready for a 12.30 cruise to Rothesay, Dunoon and Loch Long, before returning to Largs.

Largs is a charming little town in Ayrshire, sitting beside the Clyde. It is approximately 38 miles downriver from Glasgow. It is a well known holiday resort and also popular with day-trippers. Many cafés, restaurants and ice cream parlours are to be found along its seafront promenade, which stretches east to the monument known as the Pencil (due to its shape). The Pencil commemorates the Battle of Largs in 1263, when Vikings attempted to land from their longboats. This battle was eventually won by the Scots and there is now a popular Viking festival held each year in Largs.

Lizzie yawned. It was so relaxing sitting here, but she

would soon have to return on board.

Back on the *Waverley*'s bridge she found that Chief Officer Dougie was anxious to talk to her.

'Captain, we have had the harbourmaster from Rothesay on to us. He says there are reports of three northern bottlenose whales in Rothesay Bay.'

'That's not good,' mused Lizzie thoughtfully. 'They can be quite big animals. Adults up to six times my size, they could maybe damage our paddles. Ah've seen them before in the Clyde. So post a couple of lookouts on the bridge with binoculars and tell them to keep their eyes sharp. Now, Dougie, are we just about ready to leave?'

'Well, Captain, it's 12.30 and I don't see any other passengers... oh, wait! There's a huge fat guy half-running up the pier.'

The large fellow panted up just as the gangway was about to be hauled on board.

'Okay,' said Lizzie, 'looks like we have steam up, so let's get her under way.'

Waverley was facing upriver. She slowly swung out from the pier heading northwest towards Rothesay Bay. In the distance, about six miles away, Lizzie could see the car ferry from Rothesay approaching Wemyss Bay pier.

'Listen, Dougie. Get in touch with the Wemyss Bay ferry and find out if they had any problems in Rothesay with whales.'

A few minutes later, it was confirmed that the whales were still active and that a number of small craft were out trying to entice them back out into the main channel. The boats had apparently put themselves into a U-shaped formation to drive the whales into the Firth, then hopefully back to the Atlantic.

'Right,' commanded Lizzie. 'Get in touch with the harbourmasters in Rothesay and Dunoon. Tell them we are giving Rothesay the by in the meantime, we will go directly tae Dunoon.'

Five minutes later, the change in plan was duly confirmed to passengers over the tannoy.

Not long after this, Lizzie was informed that one of the passengers urgently wanted to talk to her. She went down to meet him on deck.

'Yessur. How can I help?'

It was the heavily built man who had only just made their departure. He was wearing a dark suit and his black hair was combed neatly back from his forehead. He spoke with a foreign accent and was clearly unhappy.

'Captain, I have made a significant effort to come on the *Waverley* today, at very short notice I may add. I heard on the radio at lunch time that whales were in Rothesay Bay and I am an enthusiast of these lovely animals. Why are we not going there? It was advertised that the first port of call was Rothesay, so you are obligated to meet your published timetable.'

'Well, sur, it is my duty as the master of this vessel to protect it and its passengers from all hazards. Whales could do great damage to us.'

'Nonsense. What kind of a captain are you? Whales are gentle creatures. I am sure your passengers would be thrilled to see them up close.'

Lizzie's face was beginning to go red. This bloke was annoying her.

'What kind of a captain am I? Someone who looks after their vessel, passengers and crew! You say go up close. No way, Jonah. From three miles away, maybe. I know whales can be curious about ships. So jist you listen to me, Jonah. Ah'm in charge here. Ah decide oor route. If you look at your timetable you will see that changes in destinations can be made based on prevailing conditions.'

'Jonah was thrown overboard, as I recall, Captain. I hope you are not going to do that to me?'

'Well, Ah'm certainly thinkin' aboot it!' And despite her unhappy face, she gave him a wink.

'You are angry with me, Captain, and would like to bury me at sea, perhaps?'

'Naw. You're wrang. We've nae spades!'

Waverley was now in midchannel, a mile out from Skelmorlie and Wemyss Bay. Soon she would cut over to sail directly to Dunoon.

Back on the bridge, Chief Officer Dougie had disturbing information. It wasn't just 'Jonah' who was unhappy about the change of destination. 'Captain, I understand we have a BBC Scotland TV News crew on board who were also hoping to see the whales. They would also like a wee word with you.'

'That's aw Ah need,' grumbled Lizzie. 'Tae appear oan the 6.30 news an' justify tae the nation aw ma decisions. Right, Ah suppose Ah better see them. Do a wee bit o' PR fur the company, you know.'

Down on the deck, Lizzie met up with Ginty Jones, the pretty young reporter, a cameraman, and a soundman with a long boom microphone.

Lizzie smiled. 'Nice tae meet you all. Ah've seen you afore oan the telly, Ginty. You're doing a grand job.'

Ginty smiled. 'Thanks, Captain. I just want to know why we are not going to see the whales today? It would make an extremely interesting piece on the news, you know.'

'Ah can understaun that, Ginty. Ah wis in Glesca when there was a whale swimming around near Pacific Quay. Everyone wanted tae catch a glimpse o' its dorsal fin. The fact is, that although they can be very friendly creatures, Ah don't want them being over friendly with the *Waverley*. She is a precious old boat that is irreplaceable. So, we are going to keep our distance. Once we are at Dunoon and Loch Long we can find out how things are going back in Rothesay Bay. If the whales have definitely gone, then we will go into Rothesay before heading back to Largs.'

'But, Captain, if the whales have left then we will have wasted our time coming out on the *Waverley* today.'

'Listen, Ginty. Coming on the *Waverley* is never a waste of time. It is a privilege. Why don't you go around chatting and filming some o' oor passengers? You should know that we have had many famous faces on board from time to time. Many from television. But see if anybuddy moans, jist edit it oot.'

'Will you go on camera as well, Captain?'

'Aye, nae bother. But can it wait until we're on our way back to Largs.'

'Okay. That's good. We will hopefully see you later then, Captain.'

Lizzie quickly returned to the bridge. They were making good headway towards Dunoon. However, Lizzie was always extremely cautious coming into Dunoon due to the proximity of the Gantocks, a small rocky outcrop lying not far from the pier, highlighted by a large navigational beacon.

Dunoon is situated on the Cowal peninsula on the western shore of the Firth of Clyde. The town evolved around the large Castle Mound located directly behind the pier. *Waverley* would now berth at Dunoon allowing passengers, if they wished, to explore the holiday town. They would be picked up on the ship's return from Loch Long.

As *Waverley* approached the Category A listed Victorian pier, lines were thrown from the ship and hauled in. The lines were attached to mooring ropes which would be fastened to bollards to help secure the ship beside the pier. Soon, the gangway was run out and Lizzie peered down from the bridge, keen to see how many passengers would disembark. There were only eight and amongst them was 'Jonah'. He waved up at the bridge. 'Shouldn't have winked at him. Ah've given that fella ideas,' thought Lizzie.

Lizzie opted to go down to the sponson to welcome boarding passengers. There were about 20 of them, including an over-enthusiastic chap who observed, 'Oh, you'll no doubt be the captain. I heard the captain was now a lady. Let me ask your opinion, Captain. When the *Waverley* approaches a pier, a thin cordage line is thrown by your crew to workers on the pier. These guys are maybe underrated, they are extremely important in ensuring *Waverley* docks safely. Do you agree?'

'Ah don't know if me being a lady is right! But aye, these guys are important all right. In fact, I would say they are quay workers!'

As the whales were apparently still in Rothesay Bay, the old paddler duly set off past Kirn and the Western Ferry Terminal at Hunter's Quay. Then it was on past the entrance to the Holy Loch, before turning to port to enter the mouth of Loch Long.

Suddenly Lizzie heard a shout. 'Whale just aft of the bow!'

Lizzie ran over to the far end of the bridge. Immediately, her sharp eyes saw a small dorsal fin about 300 yards away.

She gave the order, 'Stop! Telegraph reverse engines!'

A few moments later, passengers were surprised that the *Waverley* was going backwards, and then changing tact and steering round in a wide circle before heading back in the direction of Dunoon.

'That whale now seems to be following us, Captain,' observed Dougie. 'Ah think it's a baby. Just a calf. It's certainly no Moby Dick. Probably looking for its family in Rothesay Bay.'

Lizzie kept looking back in the direction of the small animal which now seemed to be intently following the *Waverley*, just a few hundred yards behind the stern. 'Tell everyone to keep their eyes peeled. If it comes any nearer we will need to pick up more speed.'

Looking down from the bridge, Lizzie could see that the aft decks were now lined with passengers, all watching the progress of this baby whale. Amongst the passengers were the BBC crew busy filming the activity.

As *Waverley* was once again approaching Dunoon, Lizzie made an announcement over the tannoy.

'Ladies and gentlemen, as you will have observed, we are not in Loch Long. The whale you can see has clearly taken a fancy to us. Our intention is to encourage this calf back to the pod of whales currently in Rothesay Bay. Assuming we are successful, then we will briefly return to Loch Long. You may also have noticed that we have a BBC Scotland *News* crew on board, who I can see are right now busily filming the whale in our wake. Having talked to them earlier, I know that they will be pleased with this development. For your further information, I am led to believe whales do talk to one another, so I just hope mummy whale is telling this baby whale that playtime is over!'

Lizzie could hear some laughter and applause.

'Dougie,' Lizzie instructed, 'Now be awfa careful. We don't want a family reunion endangering the ship.'

And then turning to the men on the bridge she added, 'Keep yer binoculars trained on the entrance to Rothesay Bay, lads. Let me know immediately if you see three whales coming towards us.'

Ten minutes later, off Toward Point Lighthouse at the entrance to the bay, there was a sudden shout from the watchers.

'Captain! The whale family are coming towards us. Must have heard their baby crying.'

Sure enough, Lizzie could now just about make out three dorsals. Behind them was an armada of small boats shepherding the animals out from the bay.

Lizzie gave it a minute and then ordered, 'Turn to port! Get out onto the Firth immediately. Here come the family.'

Waverley swung to port with all eyes watching to see what the calf would do. Follow the *Waverley*, or rejoin its family? The small whale suddenly changed direction, and instead of continuing to follow the *Waverley*, it turned to meet its oncoming relatives.

'Stay out in the middle of the Clyde just now,' ordered Lizzie. 'Keep away from the pod.'

Back on the tannoy Lizzie announced, 'Well, ladies and gentlemen, we have all had an exciting hour. The calf is now probably getting hell from its mother for swimming away. So we will now return to Loch Long for a very short cruise, but will be back at Dunoon in time to meet our passenger timetable.'

As a result, *Waverley* once more sailed past Dunoon, Kirn and the Holy Loch before sailing into Loch Long. The water was calm and the sun was still shining brightly, and the surrounding hills, known locally as the Arrochar Alps, looked enchantingly bright.

But time was not with them and too soon they had to sail back to Dunoon.

When passengers embarked at Dunoon, among them

was the foreign whale enthusiast. *Waverley* had hardly got under way back to Largs when Lizzie was told he wanted to speak to her.

'Aw. Here we go again,' she moaned.

And there was 'Jonah', but this time with a broad smile on his face.

'Nice tae see ye happy, Jonah,' Lizzie greeted him. 'How can Ah help?'

'Captain, I thought I would hire a small boat when I got off at Dunoon and go round to Rothesay Bay. No boats for hire. But then I heard a number of people on their mobile phones getting excited, and learned that your wonderful ship was being chased by a whale.'

'Well, we ended up actually leading the calf back to its family.'

'Well done, Captain. Anyway, I managed to get a great photo of the *Waverley* with the whale just behind it. I will treasure it.'

'Great, Jonah. Ah'm pleased that you got to see a whale even if it was a calf.'

'I am also pleased you will not need to throw me overboard,' he smiled.

'Nice to get another satisfied customer,' replied Lizzie.

As Lizzie was again about to return to the bridge, Ginty and her BBC crew appeared.

'Hello again, Captain Lizzie. We have some very interesting shots of this baby whale and all your excited passengers watching on. Now, you promised that you would go on camera for us. Is that still okay?'

'Sure. Jist let me adjust ma hat and put oan a wee bit lippy.'

Two minutes later, Lizzie announced she was good to go.

'We have with us now the captain of the Paddle Steamer *Waverley*. Captain Lizzie is known to passengers and tourists worldwide. Now, Captain Lizzie, today's cruise was certainly different from your usual sailings?'

'It was, Ginty. But *Waverley* cruises are always a wee bit special. With this pod of whales being in Rothesay Bay we were unable to go there in case these large animals damaged our paddles. So, it was a real surprise when we came across a calf at the mouth of Loch Long. The baby whale seemed to take a liking to us and followed the *Waverley* back to its family at Rothesay Bay. Hopefully they are now well on their way down river to the Atlantic.'

'It was very interesting, Captain,' said Ginty, 'not just the filming but also listening to that baby whale. Our sound engineer has managed to capture some of the amazing clicking noises it was making.'

'Aye, well it's a baby, so that would be its rattle!' commented Lizzie with a cheeky smile.

'Thanks, Captain Lizzie. Ginty Jones on board the Paddle Steamer *Waverley*,' concluded the reporter. And then, off camera, 'Captain, if you can manage to catch the *Scottish News* tonight the *Waverley* will probably be one of the lead items.'

Unfortunately, Lizzie didn't manage to see the news that night, though her mobile was busy with various enquiries from newspaper journalists.

Once again, *Waverley* lay overnight in Largs. Lizzie changed out of her uniform and decided to meander along the prom to sit on her favourite bench. The weather had remained quite warm and the front at Largs was busy with families out strolling, cycling or queuing for the children's rides beside the beach.

Seated beside Lizzie on the bench was an elderly woman, obviously keen to chat. She turned to Lizzie and said, 'See the *Waverley* along at the pier. Ma mither and father took me on her over 60 years ago. Great old ship. Still awfa popular, you know. They've noo got a woman as captain. Apparently, nothin' fazes that yin. In fact, she wis on the telly this evening. Runs a tight ship and yet is well thought of by her crew and passengers. Somebody told me she is actually better than a man.'

'Aye,' smiled Lizzie. 'Ah heard that tae.'

Waverley Chuckles

'Does it rain much when yer cruisin' around each week in the West of Scotland?' asked the tourist.
'Och, probably just about twice,' replied Lizzie.
'That's impressive.'
'Aye. Wance fur three days and wance fur four days. Jist kiddin!'

'Your *Waverley*, Captain, is normally berthed in Glasgow,' stated the passenger. 'I am led to believe that there is a cultural difference between Glasgow and the Scottish capital, Edinburgh. Is that right?'
'That's true, sur. It's actually all about breeding. Ye see, in Edinburgh breeding is very important, whereas in Glasgow it's fun.'

'Excuse me, steward,' asked the elderly lady passenger, 'could you tell me what time the noon lunch sitting is at?'

'What do I do if this paddle steamer sinks, Captain?'
'Don't worry, we have plenty of room in our lifeboats at £5 per person, or £2 for a lifebelt,' she joked.

'Man overboard!' was the shout as *Waverley* lay alongside Helensburgh pier.

'Help, help!' came a desperate cry from the man struggling in the water. 'Ah cannae swim.'

'Ah cannae ride a bike, mister,' shouted back Lizzie, 'but Ah don't go around yelling about it. Jist you haud oan an' Ah'll get wan o' ma crew tae throw ye a lifebelt. Oh, an' by the way, whit's yer name? We will be needing tae stick it in the log as a potential passenger missing.'

'Do you have the *Waverley* inspected each year, Captain?' asked the passenger. 'You know, safety is very important.'

'Totally agree. Oh, yes. And we even have a diver who goes down to inspect the hull.'

'That must be a dangerous job?'

'Certainly is. Ah heard of one deep sea diver who was coming up only to meet the ship going down.'

An old lady was standing at the bow as the *Waverley* made its way up the Firth. She stood holding her hat with both hands. Unfortunately, her dress was blowing up in the constant wind.

Lizzie was strolling around the deck and said to her, 'Excuse me, madam, just tae let ye know that your knickers are exposed.'

'Well, let me tell you Captain,' replied the lady.

'Ma knickers are over a year old and perfectly clean, but
Ah only bought this hat in Glasgow yesterday.'

Lizzie was mingling with some of the passengers on deck.
'And may I ask, sur, which country you come from?'
'I can honestly say I come from God's own country,
Captain,' replied the tourist.
'Well, you've an awfa funny Scottish accent, if I may say so.'

The control room telephonist in Glasgow answered a 999 call.

'Police, fire or ambulance?'

'Nothing like that,' came the reply. 'Could you tell me when the *Waverley*'s first sailing from Glasgow is in the morning?'

'This is an emergency number, sir. It is not an enquiry line. Anyway, why are you so keen to get on the vessel?'

'I'm not. I'm keen to get off her. I'm stuck in the toilet!'

7

Passengers Young and Old

THERE WERE SHOWERS around, quite heavy at times and mostly driven directly onto the bridge windows, where the wipers were going at full speed.

Peering through the glass, Lizzie was extra vigilant as *Waverley* was presently manoeuvering down the Clyde and around the sandbanks off Dumbarton, Cardross and Port Glasgow. So deep was her intense concentration that at first she failed to pick up the small voice by her side. Then Lizzie felt something touching her thigh and, looking down, saw a curly black head of hair.

A cheeky wee face was looking up at her. 'Gonnae gae's a shot o' drivin' yer boat, mussis?'

'How in the world did this tiddly wee soul get up here?' she bellowed at Dougie. 'Take over and I'll go and find this wee lad's parents. We really have to do something about security on this bridge. What if it had been a hijacker, eh?' She turned to the wee boy. 'No son, yer a wee bit young tae be driving this ship. Maybe in another 20 years. Hold ma hand and we will go and see your parents.'

'But Ah don't want tae see them. Ah like it here.'

'Ah'm awfa sorry, son, but ye cannae stay here. It's only for big people. Anyway, whit's yer name?'

'Leo.'

'Ah might have known wi' that t-shirt yer wearing having a lion on it. Right, now where are your parents on the ship?'

'Don't know, mussis.'

'Okay, let's go and see the man with the microphone and he can ask them to come and collect you.'

A *Waverley* volunteer was giving a running commentary in the forward saloon, thereby keeping himself out of the rain. He duly announced that the parents of a young boy called Leo should come immediately to collect him.

Within two minutes, a harassed looking young couple appeared. The woman was carrying a baby in her arms.

'Leo!' she scolded, 'how many times have I told you to behave and stay beside us?' She smiled thankfully at Lizzie.'Sorry, Captain, he has a very bad habit of wandering off and hiding. We have tried everything to get him to stay still but he is always on the go.'

'Well, this is a ship, madam, and it is extremely dangerous that a small child should be let loose on board. So, I must ask you to ensure young Leo here stays by your side at all times.' And Lizzie looked intently into the faces of both parents in order to emphasise her words.

Then she turned her gaze on the culprit, who was busy hopping from one leg to the other. 'Now listen, Leo. You must stay beside your mum and dad at all times. Understand?'

Leo gave a half-hearted nod.

'See weans!' Lizzie exclaimed to the officers on the bridge. 'They are like wee whippets. Cannae stand still, always got to be on the move.'

Waverley was now past the sandbanks and heading for her first stop at Kilcreggan, the village located at the end of the Rosneath peninsula, between Gare Loch and Loch Long.

Not being a holiday resort, few passengers were expected to board or disembark here, so it would normally be a quick turnaround, but Lizzie was surprised to see a large party preparing to board. Going by their equipment it looked as though they were ramblers ready for quite a long hike.

Once everyone was on board it was then off to their next destination, Rothesay.

'That lot of ramblers will probably be doing Bute's West Island Way,' observed Lizzie.

A handful of porpoises could now be seen dancing alongside the *Waverley* as she paddled along. Passengers were quick to spot them and suddenly mobile phones appeared all over the ship.

The rain had stopped and the sun had appeared from behind the clouds, so everyone's spirits rose, especially with the entertainment provided by the porpoises.

That was until Lizzie's jaw dropped when she heard passengers shouting, 'Leo! Leo! Where are you, Leo?'

'Aw, naw! Has that wee toerag got himself lost again? Right, Ah'm away tae see his parents.'

They were found wandering the deck shouting on their errant son to come out of wherever he was hiding.

'Listen. Ah told you two tae keep yer eye on that boy o' yours! When did ye last see him?' exclaimed an exasperated Lizzie.

'Just after Kilcreggan.'

'Kilcreggan! That was half an hour ago!'

'Well, Ah thought he was with his dad. Ye see, Ah wis doon the stairs feedin' the baby.'

'So how did ye lose him?' Lizzie angrily asked Leo's white-faced father.

'Well, we were busy looking at the porpoises and he must have slipped away.'

'Fur goodness sake! Have you any idea where he might be?'

'Not really. But he will still be on board, I am sure.'

Lizzie gave them a withering look.

'Where would he normally hide?'

'Anywhere. He is really quite innovative. We just don't know where he will turn up next. Last week, we found him in the bottom of the laundry basket.'

'Innovative! Oh, that wull help him in the future if he is trying tae get away fae the polis,' said Lizzie sarcastically. 'Ah'll get the guy on the tannoy to ask everybody to look around and see if they can find him.'

Five minutes after the announcement, Big Lizzie was approached by a concerned looking man in walking gear.

'Excuse me, Captain, but I was just looking at a short video I took of the porpoises, and in the corner of a frame it shows a wee lad trying to get into a large orange rucksack that someone has laid on the deck.'

'Heavens! If it's Leo then he really is innovative. Let's see it. Yer right, that's the wee rascal. Looks like the rucksack is lying near the bottom of the bridge stairs.'

Lizzie and the gentleman approached the rucksack. Lizzie was almost tempted to give it a kick but instead shouted. 'Right! Out Leo.'

A smiling little face appeared.

'If you were mine, you'd be smiling on the other side of your face, sunshine!' roared Lizzie.

'Steady on, Captain. He's only a wee lad.'

'Aye. Yer right. Ah wid jist wring his neck.'

'Come on, Captain. He's cute.'

'Aye. Okay. Yer right. Let's get his parents.'

Just before *Waverley* entered Rothesay Bay it was announced that Leo the Lion had been found safe and sound.

And so all was once more well on board the Paddle Steamer *Waverley* as she glided in towards the pier.

'Mind you,' said Lizzie to Dougie, 'Ah'm almost tempted to let wee Leo come up to the bridge and steer the ship. At least I would know where he is!'

Paddy Ryan was a regular on the *Waverley*. You just couldn't miss him. He was around 70 years of age, extremely tall with a long grey beard and with a gentle wry charm.

Sometimes he boarded at Pacific Quay, other times he would come aboard at Greenock, Largs, Girvan or Ayr. Although always on his own, Paddy obviously got around.

Over a few years Lizzie got to know the genial giant well. It transpired that he had worked as a marine engineer, and now one of his great delights in life was to watch the impressive sight of the triple-expansion steam engines driving the *Waverley* along.

Paddy had also become friendly with the ship's engineers, and many a time he could be seen loudly chatting to them while sharing a cuppa in the hot and noisy engine room.

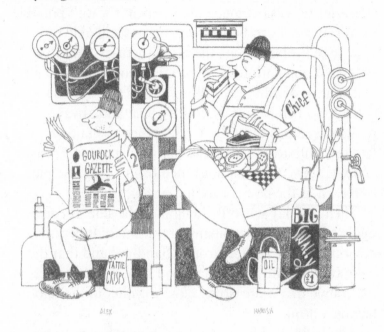

It also transpired that Paddy was a bit of an ornithologist and took an ongoing interest in all birds, including seagulls. So, if not to be seen below decks, he would be talking to other passengers at the rails, pointing out various types of seabirds following the ship. 'You know, seagulls are actually very intelligent birds. See that one over there,' he would say, pointing to the sky, 'that's a herring gull and I think that one higher up is probably a lesser black-backed gull.'

Or perhaps he would be expounding about the bird

sanctuary on one of his favourite places, Ailsa Craig. He had apparently been on quite a few trips on the *Waverley* to Ailsa Craig, and although it wasn't possible for the *Waverley* to berth there, he was still able to view with his binoculars the bird sanctuary with its estimated population of 70,000. He would also tell all and sundry why he was called Paddy. His father had come from Belfast to Glasgow by boat and always remembered passing Ailsa Craig, otherwise known as Paddy's Milestone, which lies halfway between Belfast and Glasgow. The island, formed from a volcanic plug, is known as the best source for curling stones.

Then one day when Paddy joined the ship at Pacific Quay he was in the company of a woman. It became obvious as they walked around hand-in-hand that they were very friendly. Indeed, when Lizzie first came across the couple they were sitting close together in the saloon having a drink.

'Oh, hello, Paddy,' she greeted him, while eyeing up the wee woman by his side.

'Captain Lizzie. Let me introduce my very good friend, Margaret. The best lassie oan the planet.'

Lizzie politely shook hands with the unsmiling lady.

'Nice to meet you, Margaret. Have you been on the *Waverley* before?'

'Naw me. Ah don't really like boats tae be honest. But Ah've come wi' the Big Man here tae keep him happy.'

Lizzie's immediate thoughts were, 'Paddy, could ye not have done better than this? Best lassie on the planet!

Which planet?'

'Anyway, Ah hope ye enjoy the sail, Margaret. Paddy fairly enjoys it on board, especially chatting tae oor engineers aboot the engines and following the progress of the gulls flying around over the ship.'

'Och, Ah couldnae be bothered wi' anything like that,' came the tart reply. 'Ah wis hopin' ye might have bingo an' that sort o' thing oan the ship.'

'Sorry, Margaret. Most of our customers are here for the experience of being on this lovely old ship. Plus, of course, the wonderful views.'

Later on in the bridge, First Officer Dougie spoke. 'Ah hear wan o' oor favourite passengers has got hissel a burd.'

'Aye, Ah met her.'

'Apparently she's known in Glesca as Mad Mags. Could start a fight in an empty hoose. Been oot wi maist men in the city. Cold as ice, she is. You know the type. When she opens her mooth a wee light comes on. How on earth did a nice man like Paddy get involved wi' yon?

'Well,' responded Lizzie. 'Ah must say Ah wisnae impressed.'

A few months later, Lizzie and First Officer Dougie were busy chatting. 'Captain, Ah wis talkin' tae Hamish oor chief engineer the other day and he wis jist saying they hadn't seen Paddy on board for a while.'

'Yer right,' Lizzie replied. 'Whit a lovely guy. Ah haven't cast eyes on him since the cruise when he had

a girlfriend with him. She didn't seem over keen on cruising. Maybe she's put him off the idea. Shame if that's the reason.'

But it wasn't the reason.

It was on a cruise from Glasgow to Ailsa Craig, with stops at Largs and Ayr, that Mad Mags was spotted by the eagle-eyed Lizzie. She was with another fella.

It wasn't until *Waverley* was berthed at Largs that Lizzie had the opportunity of finding out what had happened to Paddy.

Lizzie found Mad Mags and her companion in the saloon.

'Hullorerr, Margaret,' said Lizzie. 'How are you?

And how is Paddy? Haven't seen him for quite a while.'

'Aye, an' ye'll no see him again. He's deid. Anyways, he wisnae really ma type. A bit o' a plonker. Unlike Gregor here.' And she nodded to the man beside her.

'Aye,' agreed the wee man, 'Ah met him wance. He wis definitely a right plonker.'

Lizzie examined this baldyheided wee nyaff. He wouldn't meet her eye.

'Two o' a kind,' thought Lizzie. And then said. 'Well, Ah've goat tae say he was well respected by all the crew.'

'Aye, maybes,' continued Mags. 'Paddy's the reason we ur here the day. Ah've goat Paddy's ashes in this wee urn here.' And she indicated a carrier bag, obviously from a baker's shop. 'Ye see, he wanted his ashes scattered near tae Ailsa Craig, so Ah promised him Ah wid dae that. Something aboot him being called after the wee island.'

'We will all be sad to know that Paddy has passed on,' said Lizzie. 'So, Margaret, when we are off Ailsa Craig, as near as Ah can safely get the ship, you should go to the stern and scatter the ashes. Probably some of the crew will briefly join you along with myself, jist tae show oor respects.'

'Aye, whitever ye like,' muttered Mags.

After Largs, *Waverley* sailed along the coast and made one of her infrequent stops at Ayr. There at the dock on the River Ayr was quite a crowd of enthusiasts, all keen to view the world-famous Ailsa Craig. The steamer was almost at capacity as the island was a unique place to see up close, even if it wasn't possible to land at the small wharf. A circuit around the world-famous island was always popular.

Then *Waverley* got under way, passing part of the Ayrshire coastal strip, with views across to Arran, the Mull of Kintyre and Northern Ireland, and the dramatic focal point of Ailsa Craig.

The weather was reasonable though the sea was somewhat choppy, and a wind had arisen, mainly coming from the mainland.

Waverley circled twice around the small island, as the Waverley Excursions volunteer gave an interesting description of its history.

Then it was time to momentarily stop engines and say farewell to Paddy.

A small crowd had gathered at the cordoned-off area in the stern. Lizzie reverently removed her cap and lodged it under her arm. They then waited for Mags to scatter Paddy's ashes.

Mags duly produced the urn from the baker's carrier bag. She tried to open the lid but was unsuccessful. So, exasperated she passed it to her new friend to get it off. He failed also.

She angrily grabbed the urn back and carelessly tossed it over the side.

'You were supposed to scatter the contents, Margaret,' exclaimed an exasperated Lizzie.

Everyone watched for some minutes in reflective

silence as the urn bobbed in the waves, and was slowly driven by the wind and tide towards Paddy's Milestone.

'Well,' said Lizzie quietly. 'Paddy's Milestone has now become Paddy's Tombstone.'

Above them, gulls were swooping and screeching, revelling in the wind.

'See,' observed Lizzie, 'even his friends the gulls have come tae his funeral.'

As Mags and Gregor looked up, a large plop of seagull droppings suddenly splattered on both their heads.

As Lizzie was heard to say later, 'If Paddy was a plonker, he was certainly a very accurate plonker! And another thing. Imagine that belligerent wee woman bringing Paddy's ashes in a carrier bag that said 'Oven Fresh'. Ah wis goin' tae gae her a nasty look, then realised she already has one!'

Waverley Chuckles

An American passenger was talking to Lizzie. 'Captain, as you may know my country is vast and there are many places where there is a small population. Does Scotland have many deserted tracts of land?'
'Oh, yes, sir. In the Highlands there are places where the hand of man has never set foot. And there are some areas in Glesca where they are feart tae set foot!'

'Tell me, Purser,' asked the visitor, 'is your Big Lizzie a senior captain?'
'Senior? If you ask me, she thinks she's an admiral!'

Lizzie was annoyed at Second Mate Shuggie, who was busy protesting that he was actually one of the more experienced members of the crew.
'Listen, Captain. You must remember, Ah'm an old salt.'
'That might be, but you need tae gae yersel a shake, sunshine!'

'Actually it's naw aw that cauld on deck,' observed an old lady in the forward saloon. 'But the problem is, Ah'm always cauld in this weather, right frae ma toes doon.'

'Captain, I observe that you have a most industrious crew,' said the officious passenger. 'They are a credit to you. Do you deliberately keep them busy and on their toes?'
'Well, it's like this. Ah always observe the old seagoing adage, "Only the man who isnae rowing has time to rock the boat!"'

'Captain, if *Waverley* is on the high seas and she sails too far, will she fall off the end of the Earth?'
'Naw, naw, don't be daft.'
'But Ah heard the Earth was flat.'
'Aye. Ah believe there are some folks aw roon the globe who believe that!'

'Captain, I have never been on a seagoing ship before, but I have read many stories about sailing ships. So tell me, if there is a storm do I lash myself to the mast?'
'Listen, sur. If there is going to be a storm we will stay safe in port, and you can go intae a pub and have a pint, an' lashings o' chips!'

Lizzie was off duty and in her favourite pub. She turned to the loud-mouthed guy beside her at the bar.
'Ah widnae touch that pint o' heavy if Ah wis you. It'll make your teeth fall out.'
'Why would that happen?'
'Because it's mine,' replied Lizzie.

Passenger to Second Mate Shuggie. 'I've been looking at you working. You're a conscientious fellow. You certainly seem to know your way around the *Waverley*. How long have you actually been working on the ship?' 'Ever since Big Lizzie told me if Ah didnae, Ah wid be fired!'

The husband and wife were in the saloon bar on *Waverley*. It was their anniversary.
'I just love you,' remarked the husband.
'That's nice, pet,' replied the wife.
'Naw. Ah wis talkin' tae ma whisky,' came the reply.

8

The Offer!

IT USED TO be called Steamboat Quay, but since the building in 1818 of the impressive Greek Doric designed Customs House in Greenock it has been called the Customs House Quay. The customs house was where ships' masters would pay duties on their cargoes.

Over many years the quay was also the departure point for hundreds of ships taking emigrating Scots to the New World.

It is also the quay used by *Waverley* on many of her Clyde cruises.

One fine August morning, *Waverley* had left Glasgow quite early, then berthed at Greenock to pick up passengers for her cruise to Helensburgh, Dunoon, Rothesay, Largs and Brodick in Arran. The famous vessel was looking resplendent in the bright morning light as queues of passengers waited to board.

'We will be just aboot up tae capacity the day once we've picked up passengers everywhere, Captain,' observed Chief Officer Dougie.

'That's jist grand,' said Lizzie. 'Waverley Excursions need aw the money they can get tae keep us afloat.'

Looking down from the bridge Lizzie could see

that passengers were boarding using both gangways. Everyone seemed in high spirits with children excitedly pulling at their parents in their hurry to get on board.

'Ah see that there is a huge luxury megayacht berthed nearby at the Ocean Terminal,' observed Lizzie. 'It's usually massive cruise ships that's in there but Ah bet you that floating palace cost more than any cruise ship.'

The megayacht could be clearly seen berthed about a mile away.

'Aye,' agreed Dougie. 'Ah wis readin' aboot it in the *Evening Times*. It's owned by the richest man in the world. Owns half the Middle East an' has vast estates in Britain as well. You wouldnae believe it, but apparently that yacht has 20,000 kilograms of pure gold and platinum built into it. It's got four helipads, a mini submarine, armour plating and bulletproof windows, plus an on board missile defence system. Its top speed is 35 miles an hour. It's aboot four times the length of the *Waverley*. Plus there are three swimming pools, two ballrooms and 50 guest suites. The guy is certainly not short of a few quid.'

'Must give it the wance over as we pass by,' said Lizzie.

Soon it was time to cast off for the next leg of today's cruise, over to Helensburgh on the other side of the Clyde. But before the order to pull up the gangways could be given, a police car with its siren screaming and blue lights flashing zoomed to a halt at the quayside directly in front of the ship. The police car was followed by a Rolls Royce.

Four policemen got out and one shouted up at the bridge. 'Stop!'

Lizzie gave the order to hold off pulling in the gangways.

A policeman raced up the gangway onto the deck. Lizzie duly descended from the bridge to find out what the problem was.

'Okay. Whit's the big issue, officer?'

'We are on protection duty to His Highness Sheik Abdulla from the megayacht berthed along at Ocean Terminal. His son wishes to pass a message to the owner of the *Waverley*.'

'Well, officer, there isnae really an owner. This vessel is owned by a charity. But Ah'm the captain so Ah can maybe help his Highness's son.'

'Oh, right,' said the policeman. 'In that case he will no doubt wish to talk to you.'

He turned and waved to the occupants of the Rolls Royce.

Watched by an intrigued crowd of passengers, two very large men got out the Rolls. They looked around suspiciously before opening a rear door.

A vastly overweight man dressed in flowing white garments heaved himself out of the vehicle.

'Perhaps you should go and talk to him, Captain,' suggested the policeman.

'Naw. Ah'm nut getting aff ma boat. He can come and see me if he wants tae chat.'

The man wheezed his way up the gangway and stood in front of Lizzie.

'I am Sheik Al Bun Snib, first son of His Highness Sheik Abdulla. I am from the *Golden Eagle*. His Highness has been admiring your old paddle steamer and wishes to purchase it.'

'Oh, does he now!' exclaimed Lizzie with a snort. 'Well, you might be his Highness's first son but Ah'm the first and only daughter of Big Wullie Lamont frae

Govan. And as fur buying the *Waverley*, yer fether's got nae chance!'

'My father has a vast collection of ships, but he doesn't have an antique side-paddle steamboat. As you are the captain, you would be well rewarded for sailing the ship to his Highness's private harbour. So, what is the price to buy this boat?'

'Listen, Sinbad,' replied Lizzie, now in serious danger of losing her temper. 'As Ah just told you this ship, which is not an antique, is operated by a charity. Ah'm the captain an' Ah can tell you it is not for sale.'

'But His Highness always gets what he wants.'

'Not in this case, sunshine. So if you would kindly leave this vessel we will be on our way.'

'You are going to make his Highness very unhappy.'

'You are makin' me unhappy. So get aff! We're now behind schedule,' exclaimed a red-faced Lizzie.

With a snort the sheik turned around and slowly made his way down the gangway.

'Right, let's get under way,' ordered Lizzie. The gangways were duly pulled in, the lines recovered, and the *Waverley* set off for Helensburgh.

Looking back, Lizzie noticed that the police car and the Rolls had left the quayside.

'Take her past this superdooper wee boat,' ordered Lizzie. 'Wants tae buy the *Waverley*. Damn cheek, if ye ask me.'

As *Waverley* slipped past the beautifully streamlined eight-deck megayacht, Lizzie could make out various individuals closely examining the paddle steamer. Two helicopters could be seen sitting on their helipads.

'Some bit o' kit,' said Dougie.

'Och,' replied Lizzie. 'It'll be scrap when the *Waverley* is still going strong.'

The weather continued to be good and the passengers milling around on deck were clearly enjoying the short trip over to Helensburgh. As they approached the pier, a helicopter flew low over the ship.

'That could be wan o' the helicopters aff that big megayacht,' observed Lizzie.

And so it turned out. When *Waverley* berthed, there on the quayside was a man dressed in Middle Eastern garb, plus two burly fellows standing beside him.

No sooner had the gangways been run out than the Arab, a different fellow from the one at Greenock, ran up onto the deck.

'Oh, fur heaven's sake. Ah better go an' see whit this wan wants, though Ah can guess,' said Lizzie.

'So, whit's yer problem, Sinbad,' asked Lizzie directly confronting the guy.

'I am the second son of His Majesty King Abdulla.'

'Well, Ah'm Captain Lizzie, first and only daughter of Big Wullie Lamont.'

'His Majesty wishes to purchase this vessel. He will pay five million British pounds.'

'Listen, Ah explained tae yer big brother that she's not fur sale.'

'His Majesty always gets what he wants, Captain.'

'Not in this instance, sunshine. So, get aff ma boat, we are busy taking oan passengers.'

With a frown the Arab rudely squeezed back down the gangway past boarding passengers, and rejoined his two bodyguards.

Back on the bridge, Lizzie heaved a sigh. 'Right. Are we nearly ready to go?'

'Aye, skipper. Looks like most folks are on board so we can get under way.'

'Good. By heavens that old King really fancies the *Waverley*. Mair money than sense if you ask me. He's offered five million pounds.'

'Wow! But Captain Lizzie, you wull need tae tell Waverley Excursions when we get back tae Glesca.'

'You're right. But say nothing tae anyone at present.'

Soon *Waverley* was making her way along the coast towards Dunoon where she would let a few passengers off, to be collected later on in the day. New passengers were also scheduled to join today's cruise at Dunoon.

In the meantime, Lizzie opted to do a bit of circulating among the passengers. They all were curious as to the Middle Eastern gentlemen who had come on board.

'Och,' explained Lizzie. 'They are jist big fans o' this paddle steamer. We have an international reputation, you know.'

As they neared Dunoon a helicopter overhead indicated that these 'fans' were probably still interested in buying the ship.

Sure enough, when *Waverley* docked at Dunoon, there was another man dressed in Middle Eastern costume plus two burly bodyguards.

'Here we go again!' exclaimed Lizzie as she went down to the deck.

'Madam, Captain, I am Sheik Al Bin Wheelie, the third son of his Majesty King Abdulla.'

'Aye, an' as Ah told yer brothers ma fether Big Wullie Lamont only managed tae produce me. So, as a matter of interest, how many sons does His Majesty have?'

'Just three, Captain. You should know his Majesty will pay any reasonable price the owners will ask.'

'Nae chance, sunshine. *Waverley* isnae fur sale. How many times have Ah goat tae tell you lot that?'

'His Majesty always gets what he wants, Captain.'

'Not this time, sunshine.'

'Why you call me sunshine?'

'Ah always call people who annoy me, sunshine. Now get aff the *Waverley* and tell yer auld father his bum is oot the windae.'

'We have many bathrooms on the *Golden Eagle*.'

'Well, his bum is still oot the windae, sunshine!'

'I must also convey that His Majesty saw you on the bridge of the *Waverley* as you sailed past the *Golden Eagle*. He says that you are a well-structured female. So, in addition to buying the ship he will take you into his prestigious seraglio. There you will be well rewarded.'

'And whit in the world is a seraglio, sunshine?'

'It is his harem.'

'His harem! Listen, if Ah wanted tae, Ah could have half the men in Glesca. Ah'm the captain of the good ship PS *Waverley*, not an old man's plaything. Noo ye've goat me fair beelin'! You have exactly five seconds to get aff this ship otherwise I will have you thrown over the side.'

The sheik turned on his heel and marched off the boat.

'This is doin' ma heid in,' exclaimed Lizzie once she was back on the bridge. 'Anyway, let's get on to Rothesay. At least the old King appears tae have only three sons, so we should hopefully now get a bit of peace. You couldnae make this kerryoan up!'

As *Waverley* entered Rothesay Bay, Lizzie searched the skies for signs of a helicopter. None appeared. Despite that, those on the bridge closely examined the small group of people on the pier waiting to board. There was no sign of anyone dressed in flowing white robes.

As *Waverley* berthed Lizzie exclaimed, 'Ah hope the message has finally got through tae that lot!'

Apart from the interruptions by the sheiks, everything else had gone well. The noise level from passengers both below deck and on deck clearly showed that people were enjoying their cruise.

It was as *Waverley* was sitting at the pier that someone noticed the dot in the sky. It was a plane. The noise it made grew louder and as it swooped down over the ship Lizzie noticed the floats. 'It's a seaplane!' she exclaimed. Everyone watched it circle and turn, before coming directly towards the ship and landing, then taxiing up to the pier.

'The lengths these sheiks will go to for the *Waverley*,' moaned Lizzie. 'Mind you, Ah didnae notice a wee plane on board that huge yacht as we passed.'

'Naw, skipper,' explained Dougie, 'that's one of these Cessnas that a company on Loch Lomond have for tourist trips. At least our passengers are being well entertained on today's cruise.'

'They certainly are,' agreed Lizzie as she waited for a sheik to appear.

But no one from the *Golden Eagle* appeared. It transpired that the plane had been hired only a few hours ago by the husband of a woman passenger on board who had phoned him urgently to say she had forgotten to take vital medicine with her.

When Lizzie was informed of this she was heard to comment that at least some woman had a well-heeled caring partner.

Later, coming out of Rothesay Bay, crowds could be seen onshore stopping on the roadside to wave to the old paddler. Then it was across the Clyde to Largs to pick up a few more passengers. Again, no helicopter appeared.

Waverley continued on her scheduled cruise to her final stop at Brodick, one of the larger villages on Arran and the main hub for the Caledonian MacBrayne ferry connecting Arran to Ardrossan on the mainland.

As *Waverley* approached her usual berth at the harbour, Lizzie could see that a fishing boat was sitting where she normally tied up.

'Gie them a couple o' hoots,' she instructed Dougie.

The fishing vessel didn't move. Then Lizzie saw that an ambulance was on the pier with what appeared to be a nurse and a paramedic waiving frantically at the *Waverley*'s bridge.

'Okay, Dougie. Edge her up slowly to sit just behind this fishing boat, and we'll see what this is all about.'

Once *Waverley* had come to a complete stop the gangplanks were lowered. 'Dougie,' ordered Lizzie. tell the passengers we will let them off in a couple of minutes once I've dealt with this,' and Lizzie went down to talk to the medics.

'Ah'm the captain, so, whit's the problem, guys?' asked a concerned Lizzie.

'Oh, Ah recognise you,' said the nurse. 'You're Captain Lizzie. Well, the situation is that we have an emergency. A wee lad off this boat fell and has cut himself badly. We are doing our best at A&E but we need blood desperately. The trouble is he's AB negative and we only had two pints and there are no residents on Arran as far as we know of that type. We have ordered more supplies from the mainland but the emergency helicopter has a technical problem right now, and the ferry from Ardrossan is not due in for another two hours. So we were hoping you could make an announcement to your passengers to see if anyone has that blood type and is prepared to donate some.'

'Well, for a start, nurse, Ah'm AB negative,' Lizzie informed them. 'So that's at least one pint you're going to get. But sounds as if you need more than just a pint. Right, hang on, and Ah'll see whit our passengers can offer.'

Lizzie quickly made her way back onto the ship and immediately got on the tannoy, explaining the emergency and looking for volunteers to come forward to the gangway. Amazingly three men appeared, all keen to help.

Lizzie and her volunteer passengers were quickly transferred in the ambulance the three miles to Arran War Memorial Hospital at Lamlash. After blood tests, they all willingly donated some of the precious liquid, then sat anxiously chatting to the skipper of the fishing boat while they sipped sweet tea. The skipper explained the lad in question was his only son. The poor man's face clearly showed his distress and concern.

Eventually, a smiling doctor appeared to inform them that although the transfusion was still in progress, the young lad was now doing well and his blood pressure was returning to normal.

His father's face lit up. He hugged everybody, with an extra special one for Lizzie.

'That's jist wonderful!' exclaimed Lizzie, ever so pleased with herself and the *Waverley* passengers. 'But we need tae get back tae the *Waverley*. We're now running quite late.'

'No problem,' said the doctor. 'But take plenty of liquid, folks. We actually took a drop or two more from you than the standard 470 milligrams.'

On the way back to the ship, Lizzie said to the three men, 'Listen, guys, ye heard that doctor. Ye need tae replenish yerselves. So order what ye want from the bar, don't overdo it, mind you, and have as much tae eat as you want. Tell them tae pit it oan ma tab.'

Back on board, Chief Officer Dougie was anxiously waiting.

'Captain, well done. Everybody is praising you. Looks like we have all the passengers back on board and are ready to go. Anything Ah can do fur you, Captain?'

'Aye, nip doon tae the bar and get me a pint o' lemonade and a fish supper. But first let's get her under way.'

Waverley reversed its outward journey. Firstly to Largs, then Rothesay, before calling back at Dunoon and Helensburgh. Thankfully, no helicopters appeared.

It was around six o'clock when *Waverley* made her way from Helensburgh, back across the Clyde to the Customs House Quay at Greenock.

The megayacht *Golden Eagle* could still be seen berthed at Ocean Terminal.

As the paddler neared the harbour, it was pointed out to Lizzie that two police cars plus a Rolls were awaiting their arrival. Then everyone was amazed to see that a red carpet had been laid from the Rolls to *Waverley*'s landing berth.

'Aw naw. Don't tell me that the King himself is now going to make an offer,' moaned Lizzie.

Once all passengers returning to Greenock had completely left the ship, the Rolls emptied to reveal bodyguards and an imposing figure in white.

'Listen, Captain Lizzie,' said Dougie. 'If that really is the King, maybe it would be diplomatic of you to go and say hello to him on the red carpet.'

'Aye,' sighed Lizzie. 'Let's get this thing over with once and for all. But you come with me, Dougie. Ah want a witness tae aw this kerryoan.'

Closely watched by the crew, plus the remaining passengers who would be returning to Glasgow, Lizzie and Dougie made their way to the foot of the gangway and onto the lush red carpet. They slowly approached the tall figure in white. As Lizzie did so she saw that the King was actually quite a handsome fellow. Small beard, brilliant teeth and a lovely smile.

'Captain Lizzie, I am so delighted to make your acquaintance,' came the King's deep cultured voice.

'Me, too,' replied Lizzie. She was feeling somewhat overcome by this imposing man and still light-headed from the blood donation.

'I imagine you know what I am going to ask?' The smile was pure Hollywood.

'Probably, your Highness,' said Lizzie.

'You will know I want your lovely craft, the famous *Waverley*.'

'So Ah understand.'

'I also believe you have been insulted by my number three son asking you to join my harem.'

'Yer so right, sunshi… er, yer Highness,' replied Lizzie, feeling a bit more confident. 'Anyway, how many, er, ladies, do you have in your harem?'

'Probably around a thousand. I have lost count. So, dear Captain Lizzie, I wish to amend my offer. I will give your Waverley Excursions five million pounds for the *Waverley*, and I will marry you.'

Lizzie could not stop herself. She laughed. 'By golly. You've taken the wind oot o' ma sails. And just how many wives do you have, your Highness?'

'Once we are married that will make seven. But you will be number one and go everywhere I go. A fine brave woman like yourself would be getting my very regular personal attention.'

'You believe I am brave?'

'Most definitely. On the *Golden Eagle* we monitor all internet traffic, and I understand you donated your rare blood type blood to a stricken seaman today on an island called Arran.'

'That's true. They didn't have the right blood type to give the fellow, and AB negative is ma type of blood.

'And also myself, dear Captain. I too am AB negative. So you see, we would be well matched. You would come with me on all my travels.'

'Aye, so if ye needed blood ye would have fresh stuff on board, is that the game, eh?'

'No, no, no, dear Captain. If you also needed blood I would be there for you.'

Lizzie's eyes narrowed. 'Aye, right!' she laughed. 'Well, your majesty, your offers for the *Waverley* and myself are, shall we say, very interesting. However, the people who are in charge of the *Waverley* will need to be consulted, and in addition, I will also need to consult my husband.'

'Oh! You are a married woman?'

'Aye. Ah'm married to my Chief Officer here. Isn't that right, Dougie darling?'

Dougie was a little slow to react but managed to mutter, 'Aye, we've been thegither fur nearly five years, noo.'

'A great pity, Captain Lizzie,' replied the King slowly, eyeing Lizzie up and down. 'You are a very lucky man, Mister Dougie.'

'So some people say,' replied Dougie.

'Then you will talk to your organisation, Captain Lizzie, and let me know their decision?'

'Ah will, yer Majesty.'

The King's eyes again appraised Lizzie's large figure, and he muttered, 'A pity, a great pity,' before turning and entering his Rolls.

Lizzie and Dougie stood still on the carpet until the police escort and Rolls disappeared back to the *Golden Eagle*.

'Well, whit did ye make o' that, Dougie?'

'Ah've only wan thing tae say,' smiled Dougie. 'Ah hope ye've goat ma tea ready, wifie!'

A few days later, the Waverley Steam Navigation committee considered the King's offer.

Their conclusion was that although the *Waverley* had only been bought for a pound, it was felt that no amount of money would compensate for the effort, dedication, generosity and love put into maintaining the paddle steamer as one of Scotland's greatest treasures. The answer was a firm 'no'.

The committee commended Lizzie on her action in Arran. The incident had received considerable publicity and helped to further raise the *Waverley*'s profile.

Needless to say, Lizzie did not further relate to anyone the King's personal offer to her. And Dougie was sworn to secrecy... on pain of walking the plank!

Waverley Chuckles

An American tourist was talking to Big Lizzie.
'Hey, could you tell me something, ma'am. Is your sun the same sun that we get in Florida?'
'Probably, sur. But you lot seem to keep maist o' it tae yerselves.'

'Excuse me,' asked the American passenger to one of the galley boys. 'Could you tell me where the ladies' restrooms are?'
'Port side.'
'Have you got a whisky side, too?' she laughed.
'Well, if you're asking, Ah'm on a Glenmorangie. Thanks very much.'

The elderly lady enquired of Captain Lizzie, 'Excuse me, Captain. Is it better tae sit at the bow or the stern on the *Waverley*?'
'Och, dear, it's much o' a muchness, really. You could say six o' wan an' two thirds o' the ither. Depends on which way we're going.'

'Do ships sink very often, Captain?' asked an anxious passenger.
'Usually just the wance,' replied Lizzie.

The four-year-old boy asked Captain Lizzie, 'Are you a member of the crew?'
'That Ah am. In fact Ah'm the captain.'
'My mummy says you are here to keep us safe and help passengers. Is that right?'
'Aye.'
'Well, could you tie the laces on my trainers?'

Two single older ladies were talking to Big Lizzie.
'Your paddle steamer is an absolute dream,' observed one.
'Thanks very much.'
'Aye, but we're still looking for our dreamboats,' said
the other lady, sadly.

'Is the *Waverley* a bit behind schedule today,
Captain?' asked a passenger.
'Don't you be worrying about a wee thing like that,'
came the reply. 'Believe me, we're just happy that the
old girl's still afloat. But for her age, this ship is like me,
in shipshape condition!'

Two old men were sitting with their backs to a funnel.
'It's windy the day.'
'No. I say it's Thirstday. Let's go doon fur a wee swally
in the saloon.'

Waverley was about 8 feet from Millport pier when a
drunk took a run and jump, just managing to cling on
to her rails before clambering on.
He looked up at Big Lizzie on the bridge.
'Good jump, eh?'
'Aye, terrific, pal. But we're actually pullin' intae the pier!'

'If the *Waverley* was sinking would you send out an
SOS?' asked an American passenger.
'Well, it would be a Mayday. It's a kind of SOS,'

answered Big Lizzie.
'Oh. Anyway, how do you spell SOS?' asked the passenger.

'Can I fish off the *Waverley* today, Captain?' asked a passenger who was proving to be a bit of a pest.
'Not really.'
'Well, is there any particular day when it is better to catch fish on the Clyde?'
'Aye. Fry day!'

Kenny, one of the entertainers on the *Waverley*, played a mouth organ. He was asked by a passenger where such an instrument could be purchased.
'The music shop in Sauchiehall Street in Glasgow,' was the reply.
'Is there any particular assistant I should ask for?'
'Aye. Monica.'

The History of the *Waverley*

THE HISTORY OF PS *Waverley* is a colourful one.

On the 29th May 1940, the 41-year-old PS *Waverley*, which had been used as a minesweeper, was tragically sunk after being bombed and machine gunned while evacuating 800 troops from the beaches of Dunkirk. There was a great loss of life. Ironically, during her Clyde cruising days, she had sometimes carried a

German band to entertain passengers.

Her owners, the London and North Eastern Railway, using reparation money, then placed an order for a new steamer of the same name with A&J Inglis Limited at their Pointhouse Shipyard in Glasgow, now the site of Glasgow's Riverside Museum. This new ship was to become the last paddle steamer built for service on the Clyde.

On a misty day on 2 October 1946, *Waverley* was launched by Lady Matthews, wife of the chairman of London and North Eastern Railway.

The ship was designed to accommodate two classes and to carry a total number of 1,350 passengers. She has first and second class accommodation (all passengers are now first class!), a dining saloon, lounge, tearoom and shop on the main deck, and a cafeteria and bar on the lower deck. She has a tonnage of 693 grt, a length of 239 feet and six inches (73.13 metres), a beam of 57 feet 3 inches (17.45 metres), with a draught of 6 feet 3 inches (1.91 metres).

The original specification for *Waverley* showed an oil-fired boiler, but in a Britain trying to recover from a major war, the required equipment was not readily available. So, initially, *Waverley* was coal-fired with a triple-expansion steam engine and boiler, built by Rankin & Blackmore, Ltd of Greenock.

It is interesting to note that the very first paddle steamers used oil-fired boilers, which provided heat to boil water and generated steam to power the boat. The steam was piped to the ship's cylinders. The movement of the steam entering and exiting the cylinders exerted pressure on one or more pistons, thereby creating motion. The steam was piped to the condenser where it was converted back into water. The water was then recycled back to the boiler. The back and forth movement of each piston was translated into rotary motion by a crankshaft. The crankshaft turned the paddle shaft which then turned the paddle wheels which are located midships on both sides. The paddles are made up of eight wooden floats which are feathered as the paddle-wheel rotates.

Trials of the new ship were held in June 1947 when a top speed of 18.5 knots was achieved.

Waverley was built primarily to sail on the Firth of Clyde steamer route from Craigendoran pier up Loch Long to Arrochar. The maiden voyage on Monday 16 June 1947 was to Loch Goil and Loch Long, Lochgoilhead and Arrochar. During this first season, she sailed to Arrochar six times a week and wore the London and North Eastern Railway's red, white and black funnel colours.

Waverley was finally converted to oil in 1957, with a capacity to carry 32 tonnes of oil. In the stokehold, there are now twin boilers. Today, she has 2,100 horsepower driven by her triple-expansion steam engine. These are in full view so that passengers can stand and stare in awe at this hypnotic, mighty monster. The ship's huge 18 feet diameter feathering paddle wheels can also be observed.

Between 1946 and 1948 she was operated by London and North Eastern Railway. In 1948, the nationalisation of Britain's railway companies brought the *Waverley* under the control of the Caledonian Steam Packet Company, a subsidiary of the Railway Executive. As a result, the funnels were repainted yellow with a black top. During the early '50s, she was used on the ferry routes from Gourock and Wemyss Bay. *Waverley* also sailed on Mondays on a trip from Craigendoran through the Kyles of Bute to Brodick, Lamlash and Whiting Bay. On Wednesdays she did the 'Round the Lochs' route and most Fridays sailed to Glasgow Bridge Wharf. In 1965, a Scottish red lion rampant was fixed to each side of both funnels; her hull was painted monastral blue until 1970.

The 1960s saw a significant change in the holidaying pattern of many people. Flying to Spain and the continent became popular. From 1969 and the formation of the Scottish Transport Group, the CSP had been gradually merging with the West Highland company of David MacBrayne, the company becoming Caledonian MacBrayne Ltd, in 1973; from 1974 onwards it has been Waverley Excursions.

By 1972, *Waverley* was the last paddle steamer on the Clyde and it was decided to recognise this by painting her paddle boxes black.

In 1973, it was decided that the *Waverley* was too costly to operate, and in need of major expenditure.

Several sailings had to be cancelled due to various technical faults and she was withdrawn from service. As a result the *Waverley* was sold to the Paddle Steamer Preservation Society, a registered charity, for a notional pound. A successful public appeal was then launched, with the result that the *Waverley* returned to service with her first cruise under the Waverley Steam Navigation banner.

Since being taken over, *Waverley* has had a lot of restoration work and extensive refits.

Although built to sail between Craigendoran and Arrochar, *Waverley*, amazingly has now sailed around Britain and crossed to both Northern and Southern Ireland. In 1981, she became the first coastal paddle steamer ever to circumnavigate Britain.

Every year *Waverley* continues extensive sailings around the country, including cruises to the south coast of England, the Bristol Channel and right into the Port of London.

However, passengers can still sail from the centre of Glasgow to the Clyde's traditional ports of Dunoon, Rothesay and Millport. Regular destinations and pick-up points also include Tarbert, Campbeltown, Oban and Tighnabruaich.

Summary of *Waverley* Statistical data

Official number: 169494

Builders: A&J Inglis Limited,
Pointhouse Shipyard,
Glasgow.

Launched: 2 October 1946

Overall Dimensions:
Length 239.6 feet
Breadth 30.2 feet (57.3 feet over paddle boxes)
Depth 8.6 feet: Draught 6.25 feet.

Tonnages: 693 gross: 328 net

Engines: Triple expansion steam engine, 2100 iHP
Cylinders 24", 39", 60": Stroke 66"
Built by Rankin and Blackmore Limited.

Speed 18.5 knots (trials) 14.5 (service)

Passenger Certificates: Class 3 650 (originally 750)
Class 4 750 (originally 860)
Class 5 950 (originally 925)
First passenger sailing: 16 June 1947

Operational Owners:

1947	London and North Eastern Rly.
1948–51	British Transport Commission
1951–72	Caledonian Steam Packet Co. Ltd.
1973–74	Calmac
1974	Waverley Steam Navigation Co. Ltd.

Eventful Occasions

1977 Friday 15 July. While approaching Dunoon pier, *Waverley* struck the Gantock rocks. It was later determined that the route taken inside the Gantock Rocks, a list to port as 621 passengers waited to disembark and an ebb tide caused the problem. The *Sound of Shuna* came alongside, thereby assisting passengers to land at Dunoon Pier. A US navy motorised barge also helped by putting high powered pumps on board.

Waverley was extensively damaged down by the head. Thankfully, she did not sink and managed to lift off at high tide. Her robustness is attributed to her construction, as provision had been made for minesweeping gear and a deck gun in case she was ever requisitioned by the Admiralty. The ship was only out of commission for six weeks.

1978 *Waverley*'s first arrival in London via the capital's iconic Tower Bridge.

2008 15 September. Part of the landing stage became dislodged at Worthing Pier. No damage was sustained by the paddle steamer but she had to leave the pier without taking on passengers.

2009 26 June. *Waverley* unfortunately struck Dunoon pier. Twelve of the 700 passengers on board suffered minor injuries. *Waverley* was back in service within a week.

2017 *Waverley* hit Rothesay Pier and sustained minor damage.

2020 3 September. *Waverley* made heavy contact with the concrete ramp while berthing at Brodick pier, Arran, damaging her bow.

Waverley Chuckles

Waverley was sitting at her berth at Pacific Quay in Glasgow, waiting to cast off.
An elderly lady approached Big Lizzie. 'I have a complaint.'
'Oh, right. Perhaps I can help you, madam.'
'Good. It's this: I don't like the view.'
'Don't worry, madam. I'll change it for you in five minutes' time.'

The customer was complaining because the weather had turned out to be worse than forecast, and was going on about it to all and sundry.
Lizzie was fed up with his observations. 'Hey you, sunshine. You remind me o' the River Clyde.'
'What do you mean?'
'Small at the heid and big at the mooth!'

Lizzie was strolling along the deck when she became aware of a crowd around a man who was on his knees, apparently looking for something.
'Can I help?' she asked. 'What's the problem?'
'Ah've dropped wan o' the toffee sweeties Ah bought in Dunoon.'
'Is it worth all this effort trying to recover it, sur?'
'Aye. It's got my bottom set stuck to it.'

As the *Waverley* approached Rothesay harbour, Big Lizzie looked out of the bridge windows and saw two wee boys urinating off its edge. Big Lizzie observed. 'Steady on the wheel now. Jist caw canny. Ah've hit a pier afore noo but Ah don't want tae hit two pee-ers at the wan time.'

A young couple with two children were having an argument on deck as *Waverley* sailed up the Kyles of Bute to Tighnabruaich.
The wife turned to her husband and asked, 'So, if this ship sank, who would you save first, me or the children?' 'Me!'

Waverley was making good speed, but was a bit behind time for its scheduled arrival in Largs. A large, tipsy passenger was annoying other passengers and some members of the crew. Big Lizzie came down from the bridge.
'Okay, sunshine. Pick port or starboard.'
'But wur no' in Largs yet.'
'Yer right. But jist pick yer side. Port or starboard. Yer leavin' right noo.'
'But Ah cannae swim.'
'Well, yer jist aboot tae learn. Aff! Or jist sit doon an' behave yersel.'
He sat down.

A woman and a little girl were standing by the rails. All the while the woman was saying, 'Now listen to me, Lucy, it'll be fine. You will most definitely not be seasick.' Captain Lizzie, standing nearby, observed, 'You're doing a good job reassuring your wee girl, Lucy.' The woman looked at Lizzie. 'I'm Lucy.'

'Hey, Captain,' said the lady. 'My little boy wants to know if you serve puddings in the cafeteria?' 'Listen, madam. Ah'm Captain Lizzie. No' Captain Bird's Eye!'

'Your *Waverley* is looking spic and span, Captain,' stated the tourist. 'Aye, I'm that proud o' this ship the buttons are nearly popping aff ma chest.' 'Well, Captain. Looking at your chest…!'

'Everything is ready, shipshape an' Glesca fashion, Captain Lizzie,' reported Alex, the second engineer. 'We are all ready to go.' 'Great. But it's the Glesca bit that worries me!'

Two men were talking at the rail. 'On yer own, then?' asked one man. 'Aye. It is billed as a pleasure cruise so I came myself, and the wife went to Marks and Spencer.'

An elderly woman was in the saloon. 'May I have a whisky with one drop of water in it, please?'
Soon she ordered another whisky and one drop of water. Over the next hour she ordered the same combination six times.
The *Waverley's* steward couldn't constrain himself, and commented that her order was somewhat unusual.
'Listen, son,' she said. 'When ye get tae 93 ye can haud yer drink, but haudin' yer water is an entirely different matter.'

'Captain Lizzie! Captain Lizzie!' came a cry from one of the passengers. 'I think someone is in the sea drowning. I think I saw a hand sticking out of the water.'
'Uch, no. It'll jist be a wee wave!'

A couple were sitting in the saloon. 'Good heavens,' exclaimed the woman, 'It's raining cats and dogs outside.'
Captain Lizzie was passing by and observed, 'Jist watch you don't step on the wet poodles on deck, folks.'

Lizzie had cause to reprimand one of the deck hands on the standard of his work. A week later, the fellow cautiously approached her and asked, 'Excuse me, Captain. Do you notice any improvement in me now?'
'Aye. Looks like you've had a haircut, son!'

'Captain Lizzie,' asked Hee-Haw the Donkeyman, 'Ah wonder if Ah could have a couple o' days aff quite soon. The wife's wean is nearly due.'
'Well,' smiled Lizzie. 'As you were no doubt there at the laying doon o' the keel, ye'll no doubt be needed at the launch.'

Two ladies were munching away on their chips in the saloon. 'They say travel broadens the mind, Jessie,' observed one.
'Aye. An' chips certainly broaden yer hips. Jist look at the captain.'

BIG LIZZIE LOOKS FORWARD TO SEEING YOU ON BOARD!

A portion of the proceeds from this book will be donated to the Paddle Steamer Preservation Society.

Luath Press Limited

committed to publishing well written books worth reading

LUATH PRESS takes its name from Robert Burns, whose little collie Luath (*Gael.*, swift or nimble) tripped up Jean Armour at a wedding and gave him the chance to speak to the woman who was to be his wife and the abiding love of his life. Burns called one of the 'Twa Dogs' Luath after Cuchullin's hunting dog in Ossian's *Fingal*. Luath Press was established in 1981 in the heart of Burns country, and is now based a few steps up the road from Burns' first lodgings on Edinburgh's Royal Mile. Luath offers you distinctive writing with a hint of unexpected pleasures.

Most bookshops in the UK, the US, Canada, Australia, New Zealand and parts of Europe, either carry our books in stock or can order them for you. To order direct from us, please send a £sterling cheque, postal order, international money order or your credit card details (number, address of cardholder and expiry date) to us at the address below. Please add post and packing as follows: UK – £1.00 per delivery address; overseas surface mail – £2.50 per delivery address; overseas airmail – £3.50 for the first book to each delivery address, plus £1.00 for each additional book by airmail to the same address. If your order is a gift, we will happily enclose your card or message at no extra charge.

Luath Press Limited
543/2 Castlehill
The Royal Mile
Edinburgh EH1 2ND
Scotland
Telephone: +44 (0)131 225 4326 (24 hours)
Email: sales@luath.co.uk
Website: www.luath.co.uk